SWEET CHESTNUT

HISTORY
LANDSCAPE
PEOPLE

CHRIS HOWKINS

PUBLISHED BY
CHRIS HOWKINS

DEDICATED TO

Dr Sandra Anagnostakis

scientist at the Agricultural
Experiment Station,
Connecticut

in appreciation of the support given to
this project

PUBLISHER
Chris Howkins, 70 Grange Road, New Haw,
Addlestone, Surrey, KT15 3RH

PRINTED
Unwin Brothers Ltd, The Gresham Press, Old Woking,
Surrey, England. GU22 9LH

CONTENTS

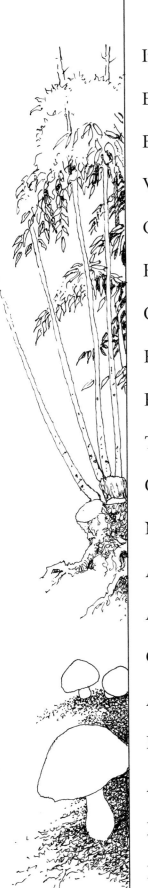

INTRODUCTION

The prospect above is from Newlands Corner in Surrey, but it could be any landscape. As we look out over the fields and woods we enjoy the view but give little thought to the contribution, visual and economic, made by individual trees. This book explores that idea in terms of the Sweet Chestnut tree. A quick flip through these pages reveals a rich variety of images drawn from our British heritage. Initially we had no idea that the contribution of the Sweet Chestnut tree has been so diverse. We thought this was going to be another of our little thirty two page books but after the first weekend of looking to see what was on the Internet it became clear that there was more to Sweet Chestnut than is generally known. It has turned out to be our largest project to date and even now many of the sections have been edited down to ensure the book stays manageable for the general reader. It has been a fascinating delve through two thousand years of social history and the story has not finished yet since there is currently much scientific interest in the tree around the world, especially in the tannins. However, this book concentrates upon the tree's history in Britain so far, explaining how the tree has been employed and some of the social and economic context of those uses. We have tried to reflect the diversity by ensuring that the book has a different design with every turn of the page. Many topics were inter-related and therefore difficult to divide up into chapters so it has been indexed thoroughly. The overall scheme ·begins with the tree, moves on to coppicing and its products before dealing with timber and its uses. Then we changed to mature trees in parks etc. before the more abstract sections on the tannins and their uses. Finally there's a section on growing your own Chestnuts. The book is intended as the successor to the *Heathland Harvest* study in that so much former heathland was planted up with Chestnut to increase the financial return from the land, during the late 18th century and through the 19th century.

The Chestnut coppices were a frequent and familiar feature of the landscape in which I was raised. I did not think of them as special in any way; they were just part of the childhood territory, where craftsmen, sheltering under a tarpaulin draped over supports, worked at a variety of coppice crafts. Deftly they practised their skills, talking quietly and patiently over their shoulder to the inquisitive lad standing in the light. They never changed their pace. Time moved on though. I left school, left the homeland, and the craftsmen left the woods. Today, very few survive and need seeking out. In their grandfathers' and great grandfathers' days, the whole business of managing woods was flourishing, to answer the needs of the country and its Empire. In about 1880 there must have been in excess of four hundred square miles of working Chestnut coppices. Break that down into the little patches of woodland that contribute to the famous tapestry of the English countryside and you would not have been able to ride very far in the sandy

districts without passing coppice after coppice. Some remain, even more are over-grown and neglected, but many hundreds have disappeared altogether. They are still being ripped out and if we are not careful we shall lose the lot. Nobody seems to appreciate them as illustrations of our working past, any more than we did before beginning this study, and so they rarely get the attention of conservationists. That said, the National Trust has been busy re-coppicing Chestnut on its estates, so hopefully some will survive. Nevertheless, there are craftsmen who need Chestnut who have to import it. New uses are being developed, so again there can be optimism that not all will be lost. The sticking point is public opinion. There's that pervasive attitude that the countryside is so beautiful that it shouldn't be touched. In particular, broad-leaved trees are revered and must be preserved at all costs, not seen as a renewable resource for harvesting and replanting. It is not just trees though. The nation's pride in the productivity of the landscape has shifted from its fields and woods to its factories and offices over the last fifty years and more. Changing that is a mammoth challenge. If we don't re-invest in the potential productivity of the countryside how are we going to pay for its preservation?

We returned to Felbridge to see the avenue in leaf but there was so much leaf that the character of the trees disappeared under the billowing greenery! Here is one exception. See chapter on Avenues.

SOURCES

1. We started with the information collected already in our database. That was very limited but it gave some starting points.

2. We turned to the Forestry Commission and were granted access to their library at the Forest Research Centre at Alice Holt in Hampshire. Everything is very thoroughly card-indexed and we spent three glorious days following up every reference. The staff were very encouraging and very patient in guiding us from room to room to find the right shelves in what is a very extensive archive.

3. Next we turned to the Internet and were astonished to find so much material. We owe an enormous debt of gratitude to Stuart Adams who volunteered to take this lot on for us. We plied him with questions almost daily and every day the answers were coming back. In particular he was able to trace the world and national experts in the particular fields that we needed. We've tried to check every statement used that was derived from the Internet.

4. We contacted as many authorities as possible to check the accuracy of the information we were getting. The majority were keen to help and to share their knowledge and this often included offers to proof read the final text. A wee problem arose whenever two authorities failed to agree with each other! Particularly memorable was the difficulty we had finding information and an understanding of 'drilling muds', so a big 'thank you' to the Heriot-Watt University in Edinburgh who agreed to help and sent us through their contacts to Aberdeen via Norway. The University holding the national records for one discipline received an enquiry from us, asking whether anything was held there on a particular topic, to which the Dr. replied, "It is not for me to do your research for you." Thanks to the Dept. of Economic Botany at Kew we got round that. Inevitably we were confronted from time to time with scientific texts that were not readily comprehensible so a big thanks to those scientists who patiently explained their work, especially Dr. Irene Mueller-Harvey of Reading University for giving me an afternoon's crash course in the organic chemistry of Chestnut tannins - a memorable afternoon. Top of the list though is Dr Sandra Anagnostakis, scientist at the Connecticut Agricultural Experiment Station and a world authority on Sweet Chestnut, having worked on the tree since 1968. For the last two years she's been a staunch supporter, and an ever-helpful source of contacts and information, and always ready to review ideas.

5. Next we contacted amateur enthusiasts of repute. An enquiry about mine timber ended up being posted on an Internet notice board that brought in a mass of memories from ex-miners, now scattered all round the world. This was particularly appreciated as not one of the museums on the South Wales Coalfield that is supposed to have mining material replied to enquiries. Just as important were the 'moles' who started contacting us - those people who spend their leisure time exploring underground tunnels. They were telling us about the timbers left down mines since Tudor times which was information we would never have found otherwise. Ex-colliers were also contacted through the helpful secretaries of colliery Brass Bands and Male Voice Choirs.

6. Finally, whenever time and funds permitted, we visited the people who work with Chestnut. They soon scotched some of the 'book knowledge' and were able to demonstrate why the books were wrong or misleading. There's no substitute for seeing things for yourself and talking to the people at work. Needless to say, we've had some memorable days out and met equally memorable people. Very few craftsmen refused to see us. I am particularly grateful to Stephen Homewood, who was partly instrumental in getting this book going, shared his knowledge and contacts with me and gave a conducted tour of one of his Chestnut coppices to help me see it through the eyes of the paling fence maker.

NOTE ON THE INTERNET

We have decided to omit the Internet website addresses used because many prove to be transitory and there were so many that they simply took up too much room. However, we have ensured that in the text we have used the key words that led us to those sites so readers can follow in our footsteps and also find more recent additions. One thing we've learnt is to think carefully about the implications of what was being typed into the 'search' facility. If you enter 'chestnut' you can become an expert on racehorses! If you enter 'Chestnut+avenue' you get thousands of postal addresses! Beware of getting your children to search because 'leather' can plunge them into the sex industry!

SHORTFALLS

Emails, land mails and telephone enquiries got us practically nowhere with Wales, even when we wrote in Welsh. That includes the National Museum of Wales and Cadw. Consequently the story of the Sweet Chestnut in Wales is probably very poorly represented here; there are not even many relevant websites for Wales. The only consolation was hearing the police lamenting on the News that their enquiries in Wales had been hampered for the same reason. How different were the Scots who responded every time.

The other country that was difficult was England. Either the response was wonderful or we got none at all. Interestingly the worst response rate was from organisations that might be described as 'open to the public' and perhaps in need of the extra publicity to boost their visitor figures. Museums were the most disappointing. The outstanding exception was the National Trust, with only one property that ignored us. The others were very informative and quick to invite us to visit, even out of season.

Industry on the other hand was far more co-operative. There were a few major exceptions, like the cosmetics and food industries, which did not want their use of Chestnut publicised and made that abundantly clear. Modern industries had to be edited out when there was a shortage of space and so this did not become an issue. The United States helped us conquer opposition from another industry and in any case the Americans seem to be remarkably well informed on British industry and were only too willing to tell us. Indeed, the United States provided the greatest help, fastest, of all the countries contacted; so much goodwill came with the replies too.

THE TEAM

I did not produce this book on my own. I led and directed the research, wrote the final text, prepared most of the illustrations and designed most of the pages. Nick Sampson was often there working alongside me on most aspects and was helpful at criticising anything done in his absence. As already stated, Stuart Adams took on all the Internet work and Geoffrey Tait translated French, Spanish and Italian for us. Aaron Mason spent umpteen hours persuading the computer software to fulfil our design plans and solving the problems that arose. The appearance of the book would be far less varied if it were not for Aaron. Right at the beginning Rosemary Dawborn produced a large album of photographs she had taken for the project, which have been turned to for reference and details for the drawings on many occasions. Many thanks to all the people in audiences at talks and BBC Local Radio listeners who provided useful information, contacts, recipes etc. Without so much help this project would never have reached this final stage but how engrossing it has been to unravel the weavings of the Chestnut tree through so many different aspects of our British social history.

THE TEXT

Throughout the text the name 'Chestnut' is used for all references to the European Sweet or Spanish Chestnut, *Castanea sativa*, and no other. The American Chestnut is specified as such.

For the sake of clarity we have followed our usual system of using a capital initial when referring to the plant but a lower case letter for its product, as in Chestnut tree but the fruits are described as chestnuts with a lower case letter. Similarly, for Hop plants a capital is used for the plant but not for the hop fruits used in brewing.

A moot point is whether the fruits should be called 'nuts' or not. Botanists do not have an agreed definition as to what exactly constitutes a nut and so arguments arise over chestnuts. The text of this book falls in line with those who claim that it *should* be defined as a nut, not here for botany's sake but simplicity. It's part of the tree's name and the fruits are called nuts in the old documents.

Measurements, after another debate, have been left as per the document we were using so there is a mixture of imperial and metric units. We have tried to be 'politically correct' (without changing quotations) and we apologise if we have offended any social groups. The former dating BC/AD has been updated to BCE (Before Common Era) and CE (Common Era).

THE ILLUSTRATIONS

The illustrations are mine, with a few exceptions. Godfrey Johnson of Eastcliff Studio, Tutshill, went out generously and drew the Speech House, Flaxley Abbey and the timber lorry in the *Going Underground* chapter. Grateful thanks also to Dr Robert McGibbon who agreed at very short notice, to draw the capercaillie, after my own attempts had caused mirth. The majority of the illustrations were drawn specifically for this project but they take so long to produce that they have been supplemented with a few from previous books, choosing wherever possible, from those that have otherwise gone out of print. The field sketches are with a fine point marker pen on coarse watercolour paper while the studio drawings are with a 0.25 Rotring pen on smooth cartridge paper.

CHESTNUT TREES

IN BRITAIN

There are two separate species of Chestnut tree in Britain. One is the Horse Chestnut or Conker Tree and the other is the Sweet or Spanish Chestnut. This book is concerned with the latter but many people are unsure which is which, so let's start by clarifying the differences.

The Sweet Chestnut has simple smooth leaves, tassels of yellow catkin flowers, and edible fruits in a painfully spiny case or *bur*. These are the fruits that are marketed as 'chestnuts' or 'Spanish chestnuts'. In contrast, the Horse Chestnut has leaves with 5-7 leaflets arranged like a fan, emerging from the big brown buds that are known in childhood as 'Sticky Buds'. These are followed by beautiful big panicles of white (sometimes red or pink) flowers, known as 'candles' which eventually produce a small cluster of sparsely and bluntly spined fruits that yield the 'conkers' of childhood games. It's easy to remember the difference because the Sweet chestnut has smooth leaves and the Horse Chestnut has coarse leaves and coarse rhymes with horse!

Neither species is a British native. The Sweet Chestnut was introduced by the Romans and originated from North East Turkey and the Caucasus region.

THE SWEET CHESTNUT
Castanea sativa Miller

The Sweet Chestnut is one of the 'big' trees in Britain. In maturity a massive trunk soars up to 30m, along with Oak and Beech which are its closest relations. They are the three representatives in Britain of the family Fagaceae. The Chestnut to be found growing in Britain is known botanically as *Castanea sativa* (syn. *C. vesca*). Currently, there are considered to be 10 species in the genus *Castanea*, all from the northern temperate zone, so there's always the chance of finding these in special collections, but they are very rare. The species divide into two groups: -

(1) the trees (*C. crenata, dentata, henryi, mollissima, sativa,* and *seguinii*)

(2) the shrubs or small trees, called Chinkapins, (*C.alnifolia, ashei, ozarkensis,* and *pumila*).

There is a third group comprised of hybrids but these are also extremely rare in Britain. Some are being developed specifically for their resistance to such devastating diseases as Chestnut Blight, which has not hitherto been significant in Britain. With global warming it is feared the disease will spread to Britain and so resistant hybrids may become much more familiar in the future.

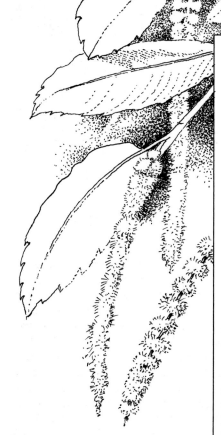

Flowers
Top - Horse Chestnut
Bottom - Sweet Chestnut

ENCOUNTERS

WITH

CHESTNUTS

Although the tree is distinctive it may be found in three growth forms:- **maidens** that have grown up naturally, **pollards** that were cut back to a point above browsing height and left to sprout out again, and **coppiced** that were cut down to the ground and left to regrow. These three forms are now explored in more detail.

MAIDEN TREES

Maiden trees have grown up naturally without having been cut back. These are the beautiful specimens standing in the grasslands of our parks, ideally with dappled fallow deer gathered beneath,[1] but more likely to be sheep nowadays. They can also be found in mixed woodlands and occasionally as hedgerow trees. Normally they retain one trunk almost to the top, without dividing into massive spreading boughs that create the familiar domes of mature Oaks and Beeches. Instead, the Chestnut has relatively short side boughs that make the tree a tower, rather than a dome, especially when growing in woodlands. However, when it has grown in an open space since its juvenile stage the side boughs do develop further to create a much broader tree. Some of the very ancient specimens have their lower boughs descending to the ground where they have taken root and grown up into further encircling trees that create a dome of a thicket, but these are rare and special. The most famous is close to the church at Tortworth in Gloucestershire. Nobody knows how old it is but it's been in the records since the 12th century and was obviously massive then, so it must surely be a relic from Saxon England. It may indeed link with King Egbert, as per a local tradition that has him planting the nut in 800 CE. Its immense size has inspired many a visitor to measure its girth, with results of over 15m. but current measurements arrive at 11m.

Nearly as big, at 10.2m, is one at Bewdley, Worcestershire, where it seems to have grown in an open space always, so the massive lower boughs spread widely. The longest reaches 13.4m before it hits the ground to grow up and out again, until its total reach is an incredible 23.5m. In all, the spread of this tree covers a quarter of an acre. Again, we don't know how old it is. There are two local traditions. One says it was planted in 1567 by Sir Henry Sidney, Lord High Admiral of England, to celebrate the birth of a daughter. The other has it being planted to commemorate the proxy wedding of Katherine of Aragon to Arthur Tudor, owner of the land. He of course died and Katherine then married his brother, Henry VIII.[2]

---

[1] can be seen at Petworth Park (NT) where they were once immortalised by the painter J.W.M.Turner.

---

[2] both examples are featured and illustrated in Stokes.

In the winter woodlands many mature Chestnuts stand out for being dark chocolate brown, when the associating Oaks are green with algae. This is thought to be due to the high tannin content of the bark, which makes the bark an inhospitable substrate for saprophytes. However, some of the coloured photographs sent from Scotland did show greenish trunks. The other distinctive feature of mature trees is the spiralled bark, which makes it unique in Britain. However, not *every* mature Chestnut has this spiralling. There are exceptions, with bark furrowed vertically as per Oak. One specimen viewed for this study had its bark fissures waving sinuously up the trunk rather than spiralling around it. At what age the Chestnuts develop spiralling does not seem to be known. A dated plantation in Worcestershire that was eighty-five years old was showing no spiralling. Officers of the Surrey Wildlife Trust believe it occurs between 85-120 years. Initially the bark has vertical fissures and these then become reticulated, before one set of diagonals becomes dominant. Thus spiralling can be clockwise or anticlockwise.

Spring is nearly over before the Chestnut decides to burst its buds, making it one of the last trees to come into leaf. Once leafed it concentrates upon extending its growth and that lasts until about July. Then it diverts its energies into producing flowers, making it one of our last trees to bloom. The long pale yellow catkins grow from the leaf axils so on mature trees, where the internodal growth is short, it gives the appearance of having 'heads' of catkins all over the crown - a beautiful relief from the sombre summer greens developing on our other trees. Once fertilised, the ovaries grow incredibly fast to produce the big spiny burs, which are conspicuous by September.

Down come the burs in late autumn and it's time to enjoy rolling them under foot to split them open and reveal the three fruits: two undeveloped ones with a plump viable nut in between. Down come the leaves too; big tin-foil things, bright gold in good years and a duller golden brown in others. The nuts need a long hot summer to ripen to full reproductive viability and so natural regeneration is primarily in the South East: that's from south eastern Suffolk and Essex across to the New Forest, with Kent as the great national stronghold. Gloucestershire's Forest of Dean is an important outpost. Elsewhere, regeneration requires a long hot sunny autumn to fully ripen nuts and so from time to time the tree gets chance to extend its normal range. This range will have varied through the centuries in accordance with the fluctuations in climate. For example the recurrent wet sunless summers of the 14th and 15th centuries were probably not good for ripening chestnuts. That may help explain the Tudor interest in planting more. That was true over the border in Scotland too, which has the most northerly Chestnuts in Europe.

Although planted widely, Chestnuts must have a well drained soil, without a high alkalinity and not in frost hollows, where late May frosts burn off the emerging shoots. Overhead cover from neighbouring trees in a woodland can help alleviate frost problems but not if the sapling is in full shade. Claims that the tree is very shade tolerant are not borne out by observation. At Painshill Park, Surrey, the estate manager showed saplings that he'd transplanted into

gaps torn into the woods by storms. Those in full shade were doing very poorly. It shows up too along some roadsides, where Chestnuts regenerate along the woodland edge within reach of the light but not a few metres further into the shade of the other trees. There are more on the sunny side of the roads than the shady sides. Some get off to a good start, only to find themselves encroached upon by the expanding shade cast by neighbouring trees. That makes them bend and twist towards the light. Their distorted trunks will fail to raise the heads to the top of the canopy and so they will succumb eventually to the oaks. They get better chances if the surrounding shade is reduced or removed, but they will retain their deformed figuration. Although this is an anathema to foresters there may be

POLLARDED TREES

Pollarded trees result from having had the tops cut out above browsing height so that cattle and deer cannot consume the emerging shoots. This was an expedient to ensure a regular crop of poles without impinging upon grazing rights. It is often used nowadays to re-invigorate ancient specimens being conserved. Thus many of the park specimens, including those in avenues, have been pollarded.

Early documentation specific to Chestnuts is scant and even more so for cultivation techniques. Therefore we know little about pollarding but Dr Oliver Rackham has proposed[1] that a reference to one hundred *roboro* in 1278 means dead pollards. When a communal resource became useless to the commoners it reverted to the landowner and when that was the Crown, as in this case, they were used as valued gifts of fuel or timber - and get recorded.

COPPICED TREES

Coppicing gives the third growth type and is the commonest practice in British Chestnut growing. The trees are planted as plantations and then the saplings are cut about 30cm above ground level. The side-shoots are left to grow on, to yield poles. With repeated cropping the base or 'stool' becomes ever wider. In time the base of some of the poles can develop roots that crawl over the original stump and down into the ground to create fascinating living sculptures (illustrated overleaf). They add interest in winter when it's otherwise a rather grey-barked landscape. There's no rich colouring of mosses and lichens, no reticulated pattern of sunlight and shadow over the rising poles, no russet leaves retained against the sky. It's a place to enjoy shadow stripes across the woodland rides and the lattice of straight twigs against a winter-blue sky.

Most coppices are not older than the 19th century and are therefore set out in regular rows with regular spacing to create the 'plantation' effect. Planting densities vary considerably but approximately 590 per acre is often the case. Older coppices can be distinguished by their irregularity. The stools will be of different ages from the practice of infilling gaps with saplings where old stools have died. Such coppices are more likely to have 'standards' - mature trees, usually Chestnut or Oak, to shelter the crop beneath and to provide timber themselves in due course. On some country estates they dispensed with standards and planted up a belt of Chestnut through a pre-existing wood, which provided a degree of shelter.

After cutting, the stumps of the stool burgeon with buds that grow out into new shoots. These have a natural capacity to thin themselves to the appropriate number that the rootstock can support. This is a valuable characteristic to the grower since there is no

sculpture.' In very sunlit sites the Chestnut saplings develop much faster than the oaks, especially on poor sandy soils, and it is becoming apparent that these will one day suppress the oaks and become the dominant canopy tree. Increasingly, it will then be possible to walk in woodlands of Chestnut, as on the Continent. Only 2.4% of Britain's high forest was of Chestnut in the Forestry Commission's census of 1979-82. That amounted to 9,900 hectares, but that had risen to 10,875 hectares by the time of the Commission's *National Inventory of Woodland and Trees 1995-99*. Part of the increase arises from neglected coppices having grown up to high canopy status, while in some cases disused coppices have been thinned to one pole and these abandoned to grow up to canopy level.

[1] Rackham, *Ancient Woodlands*, pp.182 & 371

labour charge for thinning shoots. As the shoots become poles they are left to grow on until the majority have reached the stature required for their intended purpose. Then the site is clear-felled again. Traditionally, small or distorted poles were sold off for alternative uses but nowadays they are likely to be burnt.

THE BROADER VIEW

When the Romans introduced the Chestnut they did more than add an extra species into the landscape. They changed the landscape. Ultimately, in the 19th century, there would be several hundred square miles of Chestnut coppice in England and there was nothing else like it.

Such places have their own very distinctive ecology and this in turn affects directly the local rural economy. The most striking characteristic of maturing Chestnut coppicing is the lack of ground flora. During the winter of felling, the wind is let in and tends to whip away much of the loose leaf-litter. That reveals areas of bare soil that you might imagine would be ideal for germinating seedlings, which should then develop into a green carpet. That doesn't happen. One reason is that the ground is too compacted but even where the removal of the poles scored a tilth there are still few seedlings. The reason lies in the Chestnuts themselves making the soil inhospitable. It's a mechanism to safeguard against potential competitors. It works primarily through the fallen leaves, which are rich in natural preservatives called tannins. Thus they are not to the liking of earthworms, fungi and other agents of decay, which would normally create a rich woodland

mul soil. Instead, the Chestnut leaves build up year by year into a sour *mor* soil. Underlying it are likely to be acid sands, which the Chestnuts like but which support a smaller range of native plants and that puts another limit on the potential ground flora.

As the Chestnuts regenerate so they shade out their associating flora, so it is the annuals that are most likely to succeed. The bright pink Centaury (*Centaurium erythraea*), the weird-looking Cudweed (*Gnaphalium sylvaticum*) and the pale yellow Cow-wheat (*Melampyrum pratense*) were all recorded during field trips for this study. Otherwise it is the biennials, with their two-year cycle, that have a chance in the broader sunnier spaces. The prime native of such sites is the Foxglove (*Digitalis purpurea*), which can send up spires 1.5m to compete with the Chestnut. Even so, it does very poorly after freshly cut Chestnut compared with freshly cut Hazel coppice, even on the same hillside. Nevertheless, it has evolved to colonise such bare spaces since it is the sudden increase of light after felling that breaks the seeds' dormancy and triggers germination. Two biennials of garden origin were recorded on the field trips: Honesty (*Lunaria annua*) and patches of garden Forget-me-nots (*Myosotis cvs*). They flower early and can beat the shade. Also, they were in relatively open spaces where the wind had whipped away the fallen leaves that would otherwise have smothered them. Being smothered is a problem for even shade-loving perennials, so these are infrequent, except along the sunny side of the rides and service tracks. There, some of the grasses will give a scant sword, mixed with Self-heal (*Prunella vulgaris*) and one ride walked in Surrey had amazing patches of Scarlet Pimpernel (*Anagallis arvensis*), which on closer inspection was undergrown

with Yellow Pimpernel (*Lysimachia nemorum*); a beautiful association. Along the sunny edges Wood Sage (*Teucrium scorodonium*) occurs often. It was found to persist until the seventh year of the cycle, in the study by Ford and Newbould, but on many Surrey sites it gets shaded out long before the seventh year. It always seems scarce but perhaps the habitat doesn't attract enough bees for pollination. That can be enhanced by the presence of Brambles (*Rubus fruticosus agg.*).

Many of the coppices in the south east were planted up in the 19th century on what had hitherto been heathland and so Ling (*Calluna vulgaris*) can persist in sunny patches, especially if there is still heathland adjoining to act as a seed reserve. The same is so for two other heathlanders: the Heath Bedstraw (*Galium saxatile*) and the Heath Speedwell (*Veronica officinalis*). Alternatively, the 19th century saw belts of Chestnut coppice planted through older woodland, including Oak/Hazel coppice and some of the ground flora from there has persisted. The most striking is the Bluebell (*Hyacinthoides non-scripta*), especially on moister soils or on sand where the run-off gathers, or below a spring line. Their stalks of ghostly papery white seed capsules remain long after the Maytime flowering. Similarly, Primroses (*Primula vulgaris*) can occur, and Wood Spurge (*Euphorbia amygdaloides*).

Turning to the fauna, we find that few species have adapted to Chestnut coppice as their preferred habitat. Parties of bullfinches have been seen passing through in the spring to feed off the fattening buds and they highlight the principal trend - that Chestnut coppices are places to shelter from storms and heat but otherwise are incidental. They may be included in breeding/feeding territories when those territories encompass neighbouring habitats. Thus nightingales were singing in the coppices at Dunsfold, Surrey but they were feeding and nesting in the thick brambles and thorns beyond the perimeter. Woodlarks and nightjars, on the other hand, are ground-nesting species and will use the coppices for the first spring after felling while there is open bare ground. The main problem is the lack of food. This relates back to the

Chestnuts making the *mor* soil, that is inhospitable to the soil fauna, so if you watch an optimistic blackbird turning over the leaves, looking for worms etc., it takes a long time before it finds anything. That's not a good deal when trying to feed five nestlings with insatiable appetites. Similarly, with the suppression of the ground flora there is little to act as larval foodplants for caterpillars, nor to provide pollen/nectar for the adults and thus little birds that would feed on them are busying themselves in more rewarding habitats. There are few seedheads to attract finches. There are no thickets in which to hide a nest and the openwork structure of the maturing poles provides no hiding places either. Only in the autumn are there changes, when the nuts come down, attracting grey squirrels, badgers, mice and voles, deer, pheasants, pigeons, jays and jackdaws. For most of the year the fauna offers little to the local communities, whether as food, fur or eggs. One exception is the woodcock that has been hunted as a game bird. It is a ground-nester and beautifully camouflaged in the leaf-litter. It likes the open rides for its long mating display flights when it's 'roding.'

Aerial roots from a younger stool growing down over the base of an older one. Ottershaw, Surrey.

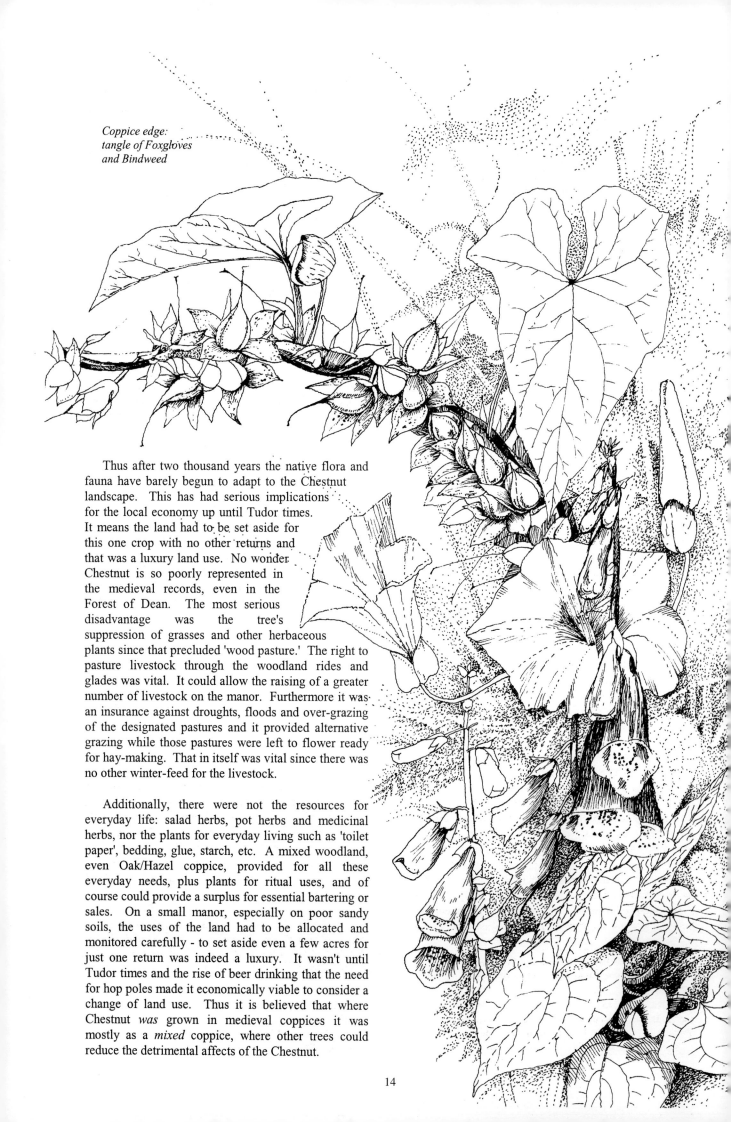

*Coppice edge:
tangle of Foxgloves
and Bindweed*

Thus after two thousand years the native flora and fauna have barely begun to adapt to the Chestnut landscape. This has had serious implications for the local economy up until Tudor times. It means the land had to be set aside for this one crop with no other returns and that was a luxury land use. No wonder Chestnut is so poorly represented in the medieval records, even in the Forest of Dean. The most serious disadvantage was the tree's suppression of grasses and other herbaceous plants since that precluded 'wood pasture.' The right to pasture livestock through the woodland rides and glades was vital. It could allow the raising of a greater number of livestock on the manor. Furthermore it was an insurance against droughts, floods and over-grazing of the designated pastures and it provided alternative grazing while those pastures were left to flower ready for hay-making. That in itself was vital since there was no other winter-feed for the livestock.

Additionally, there were not the resources for everyday life: salad herbs, pot herbs and medicinal herbs, nor the plants for everyday living such as 'toilet paper', bedding, glue, starch, etc. A mixed woodland, even Oak/Hazel coppice, provided for all these everyday needs, plus plants for ritual uses, and of course could provide a surplus for essential bartering or sales. On a small manor, especially on poor sandy soils, the uses of the land had to be allocated and monitored carefully - to set aside even a few acres for just one return was indeed a luxury. It wasn't until Tudor times and the rise of beer drinking that the need for hop poles made it economically viable to consider a change of land use. Thus it is believed that where Chestnut *was* grown in medieval coppices it was mostly as a *mixed* coppice, where other trees could reduce the detrimental affects of the Chestnut.

EARLY HISTORY

For over two hundred years the Romans have been attributed with introducing Chestnuts into Western Europe. So what does modern research tell us about the origins of the tree?

Fossil evidence for Chestnut trees stretches back millions of years. In particular, fossils arise in the Tertiary Period when the trees were more widespread than they are today. An example from Atanikerdluk in Greenland is now in the Palæontological Museum of Oslo University, and has been classified as *Castanea ungeri* and has been pronounced a close relative of today's species. Fossils for that, in France, date back some 10 million years. That means the Chestnut was a late arrival, since other common trees, such as Ash, Beech, Birch, Maple, Oak, Poplar and Willow all date back 20 million years.

There are arguments as to what happened to it in Europe during the last Ice Age. There are two schools of thought. One believes the glaciers and tundra climate forced the tree out of Europe as far as North East Turkey and the Caucasus and that it was from here that the Greeks would later take it back. The Romans spread it further. Studies of genetic variation in today's trees support this theory.[1] The second school of thought contends that Chestnut survived the glaciations in several locations in southern Europe and that from these the present stocks derive. There is pollen and fossil evidence to support this too, confirming that the tree was present in these locations some 2,500-3,000 years ago. That's long before the Roman period.[2] Therefore, it looks as though today's trees, in some southern places, are of mixed derivation. Some derive from ancient native populations while others are the descendants of stock introduced by the Romans.[3] However, scientists are still arguing this point.

The Romans, and the Greeks before them, took this tree for cultivation, but they weren't the first peoples to do so. Man has been cultivating the tree for over three thousand years - its spread from the east follows the same pattern as the extension of agriculture. That indicates that, from the start, it was valued as a food crop. In some cases it might have been grown for timber and coppice wood, to serve the agricultural communities. On balance, it is believed that the focus of attention was upon its nuts. Early Greek references are always to the fruit; not a single early reference could be traced to its timber being used for building.

It was the Romans who exploited the tree most determinedly and took it right across Europe but from whence did they get it? Traditions have it coming from Greece and indeed the Romans called it Castanea, from the Greek name for the Chestnut tree, *kastanea*[4] That name came from the Armenian *kaskeni*. It is thought to link with the city of Kastana in Thessaly, northern Greece. It is not clear whether the city is named after the tree or *vice versa*. The connection between the city and the tree is not known. It might have been the original source of the tree or it might have had a notable trade in the nuts. A better option, geographically and in terms of trade, is that the name links with the city of Kastanis in Pontus on the Black Sea.[5] Either way, these options are not at variance with modern scientific belief that the natural homeland of the tree was in Turkey/Caucasus (Asia Minor).

The introduction into Greece must have been at an early date since the great botanist Theophrastus (370-285 BCE) recorded it covering the slopes of Mount Olympus. Two centuries earlier Hippocrates and Xenophon were describing "flat nuts without a split" which are interpreted as chestnuts. The date of introduction to Italy is not clear either. One popular tradition has the tree being brought to Rome from Asia Minor by the Emperor Tiberius (AD14-37)[6] but other traditions put the date back at least a hundred years. Pliny, writing in the first century, stated that the tree came with the Greeks who obtained it from Sardis in Asia Minor, at least five centuries before (hence Sardis Nut as one of the tree's names). The Greeks are thought to have been responsible for its introduction into a wide area of south Europe and North Africa, from whence the Romans took it even further north and west.

Thus, from a variety of sources, it is evident that the Mediterranean cultures thought the Chestnut, together with Almonds and Walnuts, came from the East. For that reason, it is argued, there are variations in the names given to the trees in different places, as it spread west. This is backed by the problems they obviously had in translating these names from Greek into Latin.[7]

Illus. Genuine Roman temple material imported from Lepcis Magna in 1816 to become the portico of the British Museum. Erected instead as a folly in Windsor Great Park beside Virginia Water lake in 1826.

---

[1] see papers by Villani et al. 1991 and Manchon et al. 1996.
[2] see papers by Pitte 1986; Aira-Rodriguez and Ramil-Rego 1995,
[3] summary posted on the Internet by Josefa Fernández-López, Centro de Investigaciones Forestales de Lourizán, Pontevedra, Spain and Ricardo Alía, Dpto. de Genética y Biotecnología, CIFOR-INIA, Madrid, Spain

[4] the nuts were *kastana*).
[5] Grigson; Dictionary
[6] e.g. Hulme; pp 124-5
[7] Meiggs 420

Britain

The presumption that the Chestnut was a native species was challenged in the 18th century, through a wider reading of the old Greek and Latin texts. This led to correspondence between the learned[11] and then to a debate in the Royal Society in 1769. One of the protagonists in favour of Chestnuts being an introduced species was Daines Barrington. He was one of the correspondents of Gilbert White whose letters comprise part of White's famous *Natural History of Selborne*. To be native, he argued, the tree would grow naturally as woodland, free of coppicing and produce fertile seed that would regenerate naturally in England, and, that it would occur in early place names. Such was not the case for the Chestnut he argued. Wrong, replied Mr. E. Hasted,[12] who was an antiquary from the Chestnut's heartland in Kent. He provided evidence to show that the Chestnut *did* fulfil Barrington's demands. Indeed his evidence was so good it survives scrutiny today but then so does Barrington's.[13] They were both very good! However, it is Barrington who has been vindicated, by the modern science of pollen analysis. From studies of soil samples containing pollen grains preserved from ancient times, we know now that the Chestnut was not here before the time of the Romans. Occasionally an archaeological report challenges this view but not convincingly. Unearthing nuts does not mean the tree grew here since they could have been imported. Finding chips of Chestnut charcoal (often impossible to distinguish from Oak and therefore open to misidentification) does not preclude the piece of wood from having been of foreign origin. That said, there might yet be a pollen sample from England to turn all the arguments on their head!

There is linguistic evidence for the tree not being native. The mixtures of foreign settlers whom we lump together under the convenience title of 'Saxons' do not seem to have had a native word for the tree. They corrupted the Latin into words such as *cist, cysten* and *cystel*. Thus it can be confused today with other words in their languages such as *cisel* for 'gravel'. Great care needs to be taken in deciding what was meant originally, bearing in mind there was no standardised spelling. Interestingly, in the former Saxon lands that are now Surrey, Hampshire, etc. the local word for the nuts is *cibbies, chibbies*, or something similar, which may well be a survival from the old Saxon languages. In looking further for linguistic evidence we find that the Welsh did not have a native word for the tree either and so they too corrupted the Latin, into *castanwydden*.

---

[11] Ducarel

[12] author of *The History and Topographical Survey of the County of Kent, 1798*. See vol VI for The chestnut refs.

[13] more information given by Rackham, *History of the Countryside*; p.54

WHY DID THE ROMANS INTRODUCE IT ?

Why the Romans bothered to introduce the tree is a valid question but with no clear answer. Four arguments have been forwarded - for fruit, firewood, metallurgy or viticulture. These are outlined below.

1. Fruit

This is the commonest conclusion since the nuts were such an important item in the Roman diet. The trouble with that argument is that the particular strain of Chestnut found in England produces nuts that are significantly smaller and inferior to those of Italy. The Romans took a good fruiting type to Spain so why not to Britain? Indeed, when our liking for Chestnuts outstripped home production it was from Spain that we obtained imports (and still do) and so many people call the Sweet Chestnut by the name 'Spanish Chestnut'. The imported nuts are bigger, although (arguably) not so flavoursome. It is of course possible that the Romans *did* bring a good strain to Britain but that since then it has 'reverted' to an earlier genetic type, or, that we gathered so consistently the best nuts and left the inferior ones to propagate the species

2. Firewood

The next popular suggestion is that the tree was brought to be coppiced for firewood. Everyone spoken to for this study, who had experience of burning Chestnut, laughed at this idea. It does not burn well and neither does it give off great heat compared with other firewoods. It tends to spit out burning pieces too, which makes it hazardous as a fuel in open hearths. Maybe the Romans imported Chestnut, as a quick maturing crop, specifically to fuel the enclosed furnaces of the hypocaust systems but that doesn't sound very convincing. The idea that they followed a three year cycle isn't convincing either, since only the lower couple of metres of the main rods would be worth bothering with. It makes much more sense to wait a further two years, as advocated by their writer Columella, or better still, wait seven years as instructed by Pliny.[14]

To import a tree for firewood implies that the Romans were dissatisfied with British fuel timbers or were experiencing difficulties in getting enough. This is very odd. The Romans would have found the native peoples favouring Ash (*Fraxinus excelsior*) which tolerates a far wider range of growing conditions than does Chestnut and which grew throughout the areas settled by the Romans. It coppices well, grows fast, gives off great heat and is a rare fuel for burning hotly even in a green (unseasoned) state. To reject this in favour of Chestnut doesn't make sense, especially when the Romans were so technologically advanced. As for not being able to get enough, that *would* make sense in terms of making charcoal for metallurgy.

3. Metallurgy

The proposal that the Romans introduced the tree from which to make charcoal for working metals has much to commend it. One of the reasons the Romans were interested in Britain at all was news of our metal reserves. They knew the Britons were so good at metallurgy that they had an export trade, which had been running for hundreds of years. Their writer Strabo, reported on iron but other metals, such as tin, copper and bronze, were highly significant too. Upon arrival the Romans took over the mining and smelting centres, such as those in the Forest of Dean, but did they really need to introduce a new tree for charcoal?

In all probability they did. The Iron Age Britons were practising coppicing already, to ensure regular supplies of fuel near at hand. Chestnut, the Romans knew, would give a return faster. That was important because they were expanding the industry dramatically, to serve their Empire. Archaeological evidence points to the 1st century CE as being when "there was probably a massive gearing up of iron production."[15] Interestingly, that is the very time some people think the tree was introduced. However, little is known at present about the trees they used for charcoal, since only recently have archaeologists started to analyse finds of charcoal to discern the tree of origin. Much more of this work is needed before a national picture can emerge.

Interestingly, there persists among village blacksmiths today the notion that Chestnut charcoal is the best fuel for their smithies. The reasons they give are that it ignites quickly, burns steadily and extinguishes readily, which doesn't reveal anything particularly special about it. The belief may have come from America where, during the Civil War, states such as Connecticut, clear felled practically all their vast Chestnut forests for charcoal for metallurgy since the coal mines were held by the enemy.[16] The suggestion that Roman and later smiths preferred it because there might be an exchange of carbon during the processing does not stand up to scrutiny as this takes place only at temperatures far higher than those reached in a Roman bloomery.[17]

It has also been suggested that Kent is the Chestnut's British stronghold because the Romans had their bloomeries there. That does not stand up to scrutiny either since by far the greatest number of bloomeries was in Sussex rather than Kent.[18] The tradition of iron working in the Weald ran on for many centuries after the Romans and yet in later times, for which there is documentary evidence, the Chestnut is not mentioned. Records reveal Birch (*Betula pubescens/pendula*), Hornbeam (*Carpinus betulus*) and Oak (*Quercus robur/petrea*) being used but no mention of Chestnut.[19] That does not destroy this tenuous link between iron and Chestnuts though. The other centre of Chestnut, outside the South East, is the Forest of Dean in Gloucestershire, and that was a Roman metallurgy centre of major importance. Similarly, there may be a link between the ancient Chestnut coppice at Billericay in South Essex on a site where the Romans smelted lead.[20]

---

[14] Meiggs p.268

[15] pers. comm. Dr. Gerry McDonnell, The Ancient Metallurgy Research Group, Bradford University
[16] pers.comm. Dr Sandra Anagnostakis
[17] Info. courtesy of the Wealden Iron Research Group
[18] Info. courtesy of the Wealden Iron Research Group
[19] Info. courtesy of the Wealden Iron Research Group
[20] Rackham; AW; 335

4. Viticulture

The Romans introduced the growing of grapes into Britain. Nevertheless, there were discouragements. Tacitus wrote in the 1st century BCE that the climate of Britain was too wet and in the previous century Diodorus recorded that vines weren't grown even in Gaul (France). By the turn of the millennium people were probably trying it because the Emperor Domitian (81-96 CE) issued an edict limiting the expansion of vineyards, not only in the occupied provinces but even in Italy itself. We don't know how severely that was enforced, especially in far away Britain, but, relief came c.280 when the Emperor Probus issued another edict that did sanction growing vines in Gaul, Spain and Britain.[21]

Their vines needed supports, which ideally were strong straight posts that wouldn't rot too quickly in the ground. Chestnut has so many tannins acting as preservatives that it is the very best for stakes. Dr. Sandra Anagnostakis points out that when "you travel in western Europe and run across an old Roman vineyard, there is a good chance that there will be a small grove of chestnuts nearby."[22] The alternative source of poles, recommended in the Roman texts was Elm (*Ulmus* spp.) but the Romans would have found that in the wetter soils of Britain these rotted off too fast. It is a myth that Elm is water resistant, except when the whole length is in wet conditions. Have some of it in the ground and some above and it will rot off quickly at ground level. The other option would be Ash but young rods contain compounds that repel other plants trying to climb them. On a television gardening programme in 1993[23] a presenter warned against trying to grow Sweet Peas up Ash rods because, she said, the evil spirits in the wood would push off the tendrils! That's not good news for grapevines either! Today, the vineyards of Spain, and other grape-growing countries around the Mediterranean, are staked with Chestnut and they believe this practice comes direct from the Romans.

Results

Whatever the reason or reasons for the introduction, it must have had satisfying results. A Roman landowner could go out to inspect the state of his lands after the winter and be shown that the slaves had re-staked some of the vines to ensure they survived the summer storms. Casting an eye to the side of the vineyard he'd see his chestnut plantation and see where the stakes were taken in the winter. He'd be assured that the trimmings had all been faggotted up ready to fuel the hypocaust. At the same time he'd note there were plenty of maturing poles left, to ensure a good crop of nuts. Those would keep the cook happy and save a lot of bother getting imports. Indeed there could be many goodly poles remaining that he'd discuss whether it would be worth trading them off for charcoal for the iron bloomeries. All in all it must have felt that the effort of creating the chestnut plantation had been a good investment.

---

[21] Roach, pp.247-8
[22] pers.comm. 1-11-2001
[23] 'Gardeners World', BBC 2; 23.4.93

VITICULTURE

Roman and Medieval Period

The Romans grew grapes in Britain and almost certainly used Chestnut for the stakes. Modern usage suggests these would have been at least 10cm in diameter, so some readers may think of those as posts rather than stakes. Sometimes the Romans took posts that size and split them in three, to reduce the amount of sapwood per stake, as we still do for chestnut-paling fencing. Once the Romans had departed, officially in 410, it is thought that viticulture petered out, along with Christianity, which had created a demand for wine for the Eucharist. That said, modern archaeology is destroying the long-held belief that the country plunged into extreme decline, known for so long as 'The Dark Ages.' Future excavations may help reveal how many Romano-British landowners persisted with grapes for their personal use. Certainly there was an upturn in the fortunes of the grape in England with the coming of St. Augustine to Canterbury in 597, to re-introduce Christianity. The first documentary evidence of there being vineyards again in the English landscape comes from the Venerable Bede in his *History of the English Church and People* of 731. They were here to stay. There were over three dozen by the time the Normans compiled the Domesday Book of 1086.[1]

Illus: the two types of pruning tool shown in Saxon scenes of viticulture.

For developments in viticulture the Saxons needed to look to the Continent and so the crowning of Charlemagne as Holy Roman Emperor in 800 may have been significant. He issued his *Capitulare de Villis* by which to govern towns, including the provision of a garden of necessary herbs and fruit. He listed the plants that should be grown and he included both vines and Chestnuts. The document was circulated throughout his empire: France, Belgium, Holland, Switzerland, parts of Germany, Austria, Spain, and half of Italy. Britain was not part of his empire but influences from the Frankish court could have entered the country through Egbert, of the House of Wessex. He was in exile in the Court of Charlemagne from 787 to 802, when he returned to be crowned King of Wessex. He extended his realm over Devon and Cornwall, as their overlord, by conquest, in 815. He was crowned King of Kent in 825, King of the English in 829 and became overlord of Wales in 831. Thus the Crown estates could have been very influential. Later, his grandson, Alfred the Great, stayed at the Frankish court, and his stepmother was a Frank, so he too is likely to have been open to their ideas. Certainly during his reign there were enough vineyards in England for him to give them legal protection, in that one of his laws makes it a crime to damage them and awards compensation should it happen.[2]

Continental viticulture skills would have been disseminated primarily through the Church. The pre-eminent influence was to be the Abbey of Cluny, founded in 910. England benefited from that directly, not just through the Benedictines in general, but specifically through the work of Dunstan and Lanfranc at Canterbury. A plan of the garden at Christ Church Monastery, Canterbury, was drawn up c.1165 and the illustrations include a section through the vineyard, showing the vines neatly staked and duly labelled *vinea* so there's no mistake. Another monastery that came to have notable vineyards was at Ely and those survived until soon after 1251 when the land was turned over to orchards. Indeed there is a tradition that the name Ely comes not from eels but from *Isle de vigne*.

By then the climate was changing for the worse and not suiting grapes; harvests were particularly bad in 1220 and 1260. Bad seasons became increasingly recurrent. It was hardly worth the effort (and disappointment) of trying to grow grapes when imported French wine was so cheap (often about 1d per gallon). There were good trading links with Bordeaux for some 300 years, following the marriage of Henry II to Eleanor of Aquitaine, in 1152. The wine trade became such a significant proportion of the economy that it was deemed worth the imposition of import duties.

---

[1] Texts on the Domesday Book vary considerably as to exactly how many vineyards were listed; from 26-42, with 38 or 42 being the most frequently printed totals. Only about a dozen belonged to monasteries, implying we were growing for white wine and therefore the Church was relying upon imports of red wine for the Eucharist. Vineyards were high status and found on the great estates.

---

[2] Roach p.16

Those started in 1272 at a mere 1d per tun[3] By 1409 this had risen to 36d per tun.[4] By that time the climate was becoming significantly worse, with cooler, wetter summers, resulting in famine years of relentless regularity. It is thought that commercial vineyards were abandoned. That included the monastic ones, which all came to an end with Henry VIII's Dissolution of the Monasteries, in the 1530s.

Tudor to Modern Times

With the dispersal of the monks went their expert knowledge too. Writers of the 16th and 17th centuries bemoaned the loss of vineyards. Just a limited number of enthusiasts tried their luck on a small scale, in the hope of being able to impress their visitors. This was the case at Albury Park in Surrey,[5] for example. A vineyard was in existence when Thomas Howard, Earl of Arundel, bought the estate, in 1638. He had engravings made of the Park by the famous Wencelaus Hollar and he engraved planted terracing on the south flank of the North Downs beyond the house. The Park then passed to the Earl's grandson, Henry Howard, who later became the 6th Duke of Norfolk, and who employed John Evelyn to redesign the Park on a grand scale in line with contemporary fashion. Evelyn retained the provision of a vineyard, probably creating a new one, since he recorded in his diary, for 23rd September 1670, not only his pleasure at the progress but his satisfaction that his plans were being followed exactly. He noted that *"The Canals are now digging & Vineyards planted."*

Illus: the restored Painshill vineyard beside the lake with the folly of a ruined abbey beyond. Each vine has its own supporting stake as per the 18th century.

Viticulture struggled through to the 18th century but not on a large scale or commercially. Then two new and influential vineyards were planted, both in Surrey. The first came in 1730 and has been described as the largest in England up to that date. It was at Godalming on the lands of General James Oglethorpe, the local Member of Parliament, who had the ear of the king when necessary. Thus he took convicts from debtors' prisons to found a new colony in America, which became the State of Georgia. His estates were sold out of the family upon his death and have long since been broken up and redeveloped (although his house still stands, enlarged, as "Westbrook" in Westbrook Lane).

---

[3] tun = 252 old wine gallons
[4] Roach p.251
[5] *Victoria County History: Surrey*; vol.3; p.73

The second was set up in the early 1700s by the Hon. Charles Hamilton, who was creating a lavish new landscaped park at Painshill, Cobham. He started with five acres and soon found he didn't know enough, so in 1748 he employed a Huguenot refugee, David Geneste. Things improved but even Geneste had to write to his sister in France for information and tools.[6] They had a very good year in 1753 and Geneste was granted an assistant, Paul Ducos from Clairac. The size of the vineyard was to be doubled. The wine won approval from the connoisseurs, as did the Park by those on their summer carriage circuits. Thus the venture became highly influential. Hamilton, alas, ran out of money and sold up in 1773. Successive owners of Painshill did little with the landscape except neglect it. Scrub, brambles and Rhododendrons smothered it from view and almost from memory, until it was possible for Elmbridge Borough Council to buy the site. A Trust was established and a faithful restoration began. Progress was such that visitors were welcomed to the Park again in 1997 and work still continues.

Christian iconography has for centuries represented Christ with corn and grapes, representing the bread and wine of the Eucharist. This pencil sketch is of a capital in the parish church at Pangbourne, by J. Woodman in 1866.

The lake has been restored to its former glory and the vineyard that once filed down the hillside to the water's edge has been replanted. Once again visitors can walk along between the grapes and the swans on the lake towards the distant ruin of a folly abbey. The restored vineyard covers fewer acres than originally, partly because some of the original is believed to lie under what is now the main A3 London/Portsmouth Road and partly because the eastern side is foreshortened by a badger set. As a protected species, it is illegal to disturb them. This not only frustrates the restoration programme but the "badgers will kill for grapes" reported the manager wryly. They also scratch out forage holes all over the vineyard. Other depredations come from rabbits, deer, pheasants and ring-necked parakeets. At least low level attack by badgers, rabbits and pheasants can be curtailed to some extent by the style of training the vines. Instead of tying them out along wires, as in a modern vineyard, they are grown in the original 18th century style. Thus each vine has its own post and is pruned so as to regenerate from near the base. These leaders are then scooped up and outwards before turning over and securing them at the top - producing the 'Moselle goblet' style that Hamilton had followed. He produced a good champagne and in recreating the past the Painshill vineyard still specialises in sparkling wines.

Obviously all the weight is taken on the one post, which needs to be stout. Initially, the timber merchant supplied stakes that proved too thin and lacked durability, despite being peeled and dipped in preservative. They didn't serve for long enough and many had to be replaced with tanalised softwood. This is used by many vineyards today but at Painshill it is crucial to follow the 18th century practices and so when the softwood needs replacing it is planned to use Chestnut again, but stouter this time.[7]

From Hamilton's time onwards there was enormous interest again in growing grapes, with a prodigious number of texts published on the subject. These concentrated upon private glasshouse culture rather than staked commercial vineyards. That didn't change until 1875 when the Marquis of Bute planted up a commercial vineyard at Castel Coch, near Cardiff and then another at Swanbridge. His son succeeded him in the venture but even so, the enterprise ended in Edwardian times; their last successful vintage appears to have been in 1911. Then there's a deficit of interest until 1946 when Ray Barrington Brock planted a vineyard at Oxted, Surrey, to test a range of cultivars for their suitability in Britain. It attracted the attention of plantsman and writer

[6] Kitz p35

[7] with thanks to Painshill Park Trust for information and a guided site visit. Open to the public.

Edward Hyams and they published *The Grape Vine in England* in 1949. This was the beginning of the modern revival. Today there are nearly 400 vineyards in England and Wales.

Hamilton's goblet style has gone, from the commercial vineyards. Instead, the vines are now trained along wires, stretched taut between posts. These need to be substantial to take the strain of summer gales against the row of vines. They also need to be durable, since to replace one requires detaching the wires for the whole row. Chestnut is the wisest choice and can be seen in use at many sites, such as the Lamberhurst Vineyard in Kent (illus. this page). There you'll find where some 25 acres of vines, beautifully landscaped and maintained, and supported in this way.[8] To walk up their stony trackway, through the broken shadows of the marginal oaks, and out among the airy alleys of the vineyard, is to enjoy the English landscape in a way that has been possible, on and off, for two thousand years.

Tree Stakes

Not only vines need stakes but sapling trees as well. Back in the early 1990s it was said that we were using some 20 million stakes a year to support the plastic rabbit guards round newly planted trees. These are little maiden specimens, perhaps half a metre high at the most. Twenty-five years on and that interest in planting new trees has multiplied several times over but no precise statistics are available. Nevertheless, you cannot travel far in the countryside without passing an army of the pale supported guards. Obviously there's a demand for several million such stakes a year. There's a further demand for stout stakes to support freshly planted saplings, beyond the size that normally gets a rabbit guard. These include the specimens sold through garden centres for home use, whether ornamental trees and shrubs, or fruit trees. A large proportion of these stakes is made from softwood. Despite being impregnated with preservatives they still rot off in the ground at an early stage. This is not such a disadvantage if the stake is for a rabbit guard and the sapling has outgrown the need, but it is not satisfactory for the larger saplings. For these it is well worth paying the higher price for stakes made of Chestnut. These are far more durable and do not need preservatives. Indeed the timber tends to repel them so it is money wasted. The public seems to be aware of this and creates a demand for this coppice product, judging from the number of companies with Internet websites offering them.

[8] with thanks for their co-operation; visitors welcome.

GOING UNDERGROUND

Chestnut in the iron and coal industries and related land management

One of the reasons proposed for the Romans having introduced the Chestnut is as fuel (charcoal) for their iron bloomeries. The evidence doesn't look very convincing today in the Chestnut's heartland of Kent. There were more bloomeries in Sussex. Maybe the Chestnut has survived better in Kent than in Sussex. A much more convincing story comes from the Chestnut's other heartland in Gloucestershire's Forest of Dean. That will now be looked at in more detail.

Firstly, we need to remember that Britain's iron was one of the products listed by the Roman writer Strabo and that this, in part, is believed to have lured the Romans across the Channel. In other words, he was talking about the work of Britain's Iron Age culture. It's easy to forget that mining is one of our oldest industries. Stone Age man sank shafts to mine flints. They were literally the 'cutting edge' of his technology.

By the end of that epoch Stone Age Man was so discerning of geology that he could distinguish metal ores, such as copper and tin, from other rocks. He learnt to work them to produce the alloy bronze. That led to such significant developments we call the next period the Bronze Age. It's a mistake to think this was primitive; go to the Great Orme in North Wales and see the stunning copper mines. Archaeologists expect to rediscover some thirty miles of tunnels through the solid rock and they've calculated that the bronze produced was far in excess of domestic needs. They must have traded with the Continent. A large Stone Age boat, so cleverly jointed together and tied with Yew twigs, has been discovered at Dover. They needed boats like that to get the tin from Cornwall to alloy with the copper for making the bronze. This was certainly not a primitive society. It was highly organised.

When those Bronze Age smiths discovered that a greater heat could be obtained from charcoal than wood fuel they were able to work the more demanding iron ore. That accelerated societies into the Iron Age and British smiths continued to hold a high reputation through Europe. Ultimately this gets reported to Strabo and in due course the Romans land in South East England. They are soon working iron there in order to maintain their weaponry etc. and in due course pushed their front line westwards. They could have paused on the Cotswolds, at say Birdlip, and looked across the Vale of Severn to the high ground of the Forest of Dean. They could have seen the smoke rising from the iron workings, dark against the western sky.

Illus. View from Birdlip, hazy day 1980s

Flaxley Abbey today. Illus. by Godfrey Johnson, reproduced by permission.

The British[1] had been mining iron and coal here for some 700 years. The expertise must have been impressive but then so must the devastation of the landscape, as soon many trees were needed for the charcoal. Rather than deforesting lands further and further afield the Iron Age people practised coppicing. That would have been familiar to the Romans who would have soon realised that their Chestnut trees could be worked on a faster rotation than native British trees. Here is an incentive to introduce the tree.

The Romans took control but this must surely be a prime occasion when the Romans worked in co-operation with the British rather than suppressing them. The Romans *needed* the 700 years of experience and expertise held by the Silures. Certainly work continued. When Chestnut charcoal became available the smiths no doubt adjusted to its tendency to flake badly. Maybe they preferred that. The different calorific value would not have been a problem either. Mines were extended.[2] The pits sank 100 feet into the ground. The spoil heaps rose 100 feet high.[3] What an amazing landscape it must have been. The deep scars are still there, at the Scowles, and maybe that name is a relic from the British miners since it might derive from the Welsh *ysgil* meaning recess. Alternatively, it might be much later and derive from the Saxon *crowll* for cave. The ore came to be known as *mine* and so the original *miners* worked iron not coal. The Dean was a particularly favoured site since the ore was mixed with limestone that was needed as a flux during the processing.

It was still a prime area in the early Middle Ages and so it presumably persisted after the Romans had left, through the Saxon period. Sadly, little is known about Saxon ironworking; only three sites in Britain are known to archaeologists. In the early Middle Ages the Forest of Dean was certainly a key area and remained so for several more hundreds of years. In a grant of tithe of chestnuts by Henry II to Flaxley Abbey there was the condition that the trees should not be felled and used for charcoal. Perhaps that was a frustration to the monks seeing as they had interests in the iron industry. The Crown took a keen interest in the Forest simply because so much iron was needed just to maintain the realm: weapons, chain mail, armour, harness fastenings, horse shoes and nails for fixing them, etc. The miners provided another service too. They were recruited as sappers to undermine castle defences during sieges. They tunnelled into the ramparts, right under the walls and towers, ensuring the downward thrust was taken on 'pit props', which were then set on fire so that when they collapsed the whole lot came down. That's what happened at Rochester in Kent. The great Norman castle has square corner towers except one, which is round, from being a later rebuild in a different style. The original collapsed through the efforts of the sappers working for King John when he besieged the castle for two months in 1215. To ensure their pit props burned well the sappers larded them with the "fat of forty pigs".

---

[1] when the Romans arrived this was the territory of the Silures.

[2] At Lydney, archaeologists excavating a Roman-British hut (3rd century) found entrance to the shaft of an iron mine. There was a total of thirty eight coins in it, to aid with dating. Additional evidence has come from Lydney too.

[3] the spoil heaps were recycled in the 19th century as the Roman system left so much iron behind.

The Speech House
by Godfrey Johnson

Another instance took place at Berwick-on-Tweed on behalf of Edward I (r.1272-1307)[4]. For sappers he recruited the miners of Dean and in recognition of their service he rewarded them by putting their traditional rights and customs and practices into law. Such a safeguard and benefit was bestowed upon other miners in Europe but this is the only instance in the history of Britain. The legislation covered originally three classes: the Free Miners who worked iron, coal and stone, the Free Colliers who worked coal and stone, and the Free Quarrymen who worked stone only. They eventually all became known as Free Miners and they still exist and still mine today.

The original criteria for being accepted as a Free Miner still apply. Application is open only to males, over the age of twenty one, who have been born[5] within the administrative area known as the Hundred of St. Briavels, and to have worked in a mine therein for a year and a day. The Hundred covered the whole of the Dean. The mining areas are parcelled out into areas known as *gawles* or *gales* and miners, or *galees,* can work only within their particular gale. The overseer is the *gaveller,*[6] an office appointed by the Crown, and currently held by the Forestry Commission. There is a Deputy Gaveller who works the administration and his office is in Coleford. Anyone wishing to visit a gale still needs to apply to him for the necessary sanction. He and the galees work together through Freeminers Courts.

These courts were held originally on site in the Forest clearings but eventually became fixed at a royal hunting lodge, built in 1676 for Charles II, and known appropriately as the Speech House. It's isolated in the woods near Coleford and is now a hotel. The miners' court is used as a dining room since the court only sits on a few occasions during the year. The larger dining room is the Verderers' Court, complete with raised dais and benches,[7] and that governs the use of trees. It is thought that the office of verderer was instituted by King Cnut (r.1016-35) to provide overseers of the royal hunting grounds.[8] They were responsible for 'vert and venison', for the verdure (hence verderer) and the deer. Thus they balanced the usage of the landscape, on the one hand maintaining great open spaces for the chase during hunting expeditions and on the other hand safeguarding enough wooded areas to provide shelter, browse and breeding sites for the deer. These were not to be stripped by the charcoal burners.

---

[4] The earliest surviving transcript doesn't make clear which King Edward was responsible but from the Berwick reference it is taken to be Edward I. There were then at least 59 mines operating.

[5] there is a problem now over the birthright, since the last maternity hospital in the Hundred has been closed.

[6] gavelkind was a system of land tenure

---

[7] the Speech House is the oldest functioning court in Britain

[8] The earliest reference to those of the Royal Forest of Dean is from 1216.

The Verderers are still elected, by the appropriate Freeholders, through the office of the Sheriff of Gloucestershire. Other legal matters were the jurisdiction of the Royal Constable, who attended the courts, and was based at St Briavels Castle (*Ills*). That too can be visited, as it is now a youth hostel.

Verderers are found beyond the Forest of Dean, such as in the New Forest of Hampshire, but the Dean miners have always been unique in Britain.[39] Through such institutions we get an insight into ancient systems of land management, to maximise and yet perpetuate the return from the resources. Deer apart, the trees weren't just needed by the charcoal burners in order to fuel the iron industry but also by the coal miners to shore up their tunnels. Coal mining in the Dean, like iron mining, was started by the Silures and the Romans took that over too. Coal has been found at the villas out in the Gloucestershire countryside where it was used for domestic heating. There is an important difference between mining iron and coal. The former is worked out of solid rock whereas coal lies bedded with shales and clays. These come crashing down on top of miners if they are not supported. Three types of timber were needed. Firstly, the upright 'pit props' or *sets* which are stationed along the sides of the tunnel, and set at a slight inward incline. They support horizontal wooden lintels called *flats* and over these were run poles or *runners*, to support loose material in the roof and to spread the weight. These are still needed in the small mines.[40] Larger concerns turned ultimately to concrete and steel. Nevertheless, miners prefer timber because it *talks* - it creaks and groans a warning that it is bearing its maximum load.

St. Briavels Castle, formerly the administrative centre of the Forest of Dean, where the Court of Mine Law was held before it was moved to the Speech House. The Castle was founded by Milo FitzWalter, Earl of Hereford, in the 12th century; the gatehouse shown here dates from 1275.

---

[9] and there were only a few instances on the Continent
[10] there were 221 in 1856.

PIT PROPS

Chestnut could have provided all three types of supports: sets, flats and runners (these names vary regionally; so sets can be posts, flats can be collars, runners can be lagging, etc. For the sets and flats it would have needed to be coppiced on a longer rotation cycle than for charcoal. The thin material could still be used for charcoal and intermediate material could have gone down the mines as runners. From the woodsman's viewpoint there was therefore very little waste. From the mine carpenters' viewpoint the Chestnut lengths would cleave smartly in half to provide the flat surface for fixing on the sawn tops of the sets to create the lintel. It could also be used behind the sets to line the walls where such was needed. This last usage persisted after the introduction of steel arches. It is the one remembered, albeit rather vaguely, by retired miners in South Wales and Kent. In particular, they incline to the use being an expedient in the Second World War when there were difficulties over supplies of softwood. Its use in the Forest of Dean is far more certain, since Chestnut is so slow to rot and the Dean mines are very wet. Damping down the dust has never been a concern there. The problem has always been pumping out the water and this eventually made the operation uneconomic in deep mines, when they had to pump out 100 tons of water for every ton of coal.

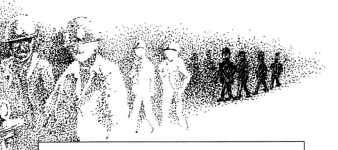

MINE HAULAGE

The Dean mines may have employed hurdlers in the early days, using chestnut to make woven panels for shoring up the sides of open-cast pits, to provide a walkway over muddy routes and maybe even as the original sledges for the removal of coal, ore and spoil.

Narrow gauge railways superseded sledges, where the mine was large enough to take them. Thus there was a demand for railway sleepers and this is one of the products that earlier writers listed among the uses of Chestnut. It doesn't sound very convincing. Our Chestnuts were grown as coppices and therefore the poles would have needed to be very mature before they would provide balks large enough for sleepers, even for the smaller sleepers of narrow-gauge railways. The landowner could have got a return off his land at a far earlier date if he sold off younger poles for other uses. Furthermore, there would have been a high risk of the sleeper splitting when the great nails were driven in for fixing the track. It is more likely that this usage has crept into the British lists from American sources. The United States made great use of Chestnut for sleepers (which they call *ties*) but then they had masses of great forest trees to fell and provide them with substantial balks resistant to splitting.

Similarly, earlier lists of uses include 'trucks' and 'wagons'. Researches into the materials used by wainwrights, cartwrights and even wheelwrights proved unrewarding. Then public pleas for information returned the belief that these references are to mine vehicles. The working skills of making those have long since disappeared, since the Victorians were quick to use durable steel instead - as per the illustration.

EAST KENT COALFIELD

Chestnut's other stronghold, in Kent, Surrey and Sussex is adjacent to the East Kent Coalfield and coppice workers in those counties remember sending off Chestnut to the collieries right up to their closures in the 1980s. Finding out what happened to it once the lorries entered the colliery gates needs further investigation. Indeed, nationally, it is an aspect of mining that the historians have largely ignored to date. Some ex-miners from Kent have 'vague recollections' of Chestnut being used to line and shore up the workings but nobody was very definite about this.

Unlike the Forest of Dean, the collieries in Kent were not ancient and therefore did not have long-held local traditions attached to them. It was in 1801 that lignite was found at Heathfield in Sussex and that led to a search for coal, from Horsham in West Sussex eastwards to the Kent coastline. Results were not spectacular but there was mining by the 1840s. The most encouraging finds were around Dover and resulted in the first significant mine, the Shakespeare Colliery, in 1890. Across the sea they were making significant finds in Belgium and in France. These were all at a great depth and so we started sinking deep bore holes, beginning at Bexhill, East Sussex, in 1904. Again the results were disappointing except at Dover. Over forty bore holes were sunk and gave rise to the Betteshanger, Chislet, Snowdown and Tilmanstone

End of an era; 1980s pit closures: surveyors and bulldozers move into Merthyr West

collieries. This was enough, however, to raise hopes and plans for great industrial developments, ranging from New Towns to a steel works, with Richborough to be developed as a the main port for exports, just like Cardiff which was exporting more coal than any other port in the world. Indeed East Kent looked all set to become another South Wales.

SOUTH WALES COALFIELD

This is another area where oral evidence informs us that Chestnut was brought into the mines but where documentary evidence is difficult to trace. Of course most documentation is from the late period, from the time of concrete and steel rather than wooden pit props, especially in the big South Wales collieries. Even so, thousands of wooden props were still being used, and this persisted until the Thatcher Government closed the mines. Softwoods were the normal provision since these were purpose-grown in great plantations to satisfy the contracts from the mines. This was especially so after 1919 when the Government established the Forestry Commission specifically to promote home-grown timber, in the wake of the First World War.

Softwood extraction, Forest of Dean
Illustration by Godfrey Johnson

HARDWOODS VERSUS SOFTWOODS

In the days when mines were relatively small and privately owned a wide range of timbers was utilised. This, presumably, depended upon cost and local availability. Where timber has survived it can be identified readily since the bark was left on. Thus at Coleorton (Leics) the Tudor workings reveal oak as the main timber. Through the 19th century the evolution of large mining companies accelerated. They issued substantial contracts for timber, despite the increasing use of concrete and steel. To satisfy demands there were many landowners keen to plant up their estates with plantations of trees, for commerce. It was a means of earning a return off lands unsuited to much else that was profitable, from southern heathlands to northern moorlands. In the south eastern counties and those of the south west Midlands there was a huge demand for poles from the local hop-growers. Their industry was at its peak. Elsewhere the demand was from other industries, including mining. Landowners planted up many acres of softwoods since the timber was serviceable and the financial return fast enough. Incentive also came from France, where they too were expanding their mining industry but also the supporting industries like timber production. Despite their enthusiasm for Chestnut they were also planting up vast areas of softwoods - *Pinus maritima* in the south west for example. Britain was importing some 580,000 tons of it per anum in the 1880s, so that Select Committees were opining, by 1896, that we should grow our own, and set up a National School of Forestry. The First World War interrupted progress and stripped the country of timber. A lot of Chestnut went to the front to line trenches. After the war the Forestry Commission was set up, in 1919, to replenish British timber reserves.

It was during the Second World War that Chestnut came back into use. It was in 1936 that *"it was realised that pitwood would be a vitally urgent requirement in the maintenance of the coal trade and that mining timber supplies must be dealt with separately."*[11] Thus the Central Pitwood Committee was established, under the Department for the Control of Timber Supply. They created eight Pitwood Districts, each with a District Pitwood Officer, in the coal mining areas. Provision was manageable at first since we were continuing to import mine timber from the Baltic region, into the docks at Hull. Then in 1941 the ships in the docks became the targets for enemy bombers, and the government officers were persuaded abruptly to review the whole question of supply. The Timber Control Board was established *"with the object of urging forward production of home-grown supplies, particularly for the mining industry."*[12] So much energy was directed into this that House reports, *"The supply of home-grown sawn timber could not be expected to increase appreciably, owing to available labour being concentrated on pitwood."* The emphasis was upon pit props and the specification for these was from 2ft 6in to 9ft.[13] Millions of cubic feet were produced and Chestnut was included, although *"pitprop production from chestnut yielded a considerably lower profit than for any other form of its utilization during the war."*[14]

After the war, the main collieries were nationalised with the establishment of the National Coal Board in 1947. That worked with the Forestry Commission for the provision of mine timber and that was primarily from the conifer plantations. In most places Chestnut was forgotten.

---

[11] House; *Timber at War*
[12] House
[13] Muir; p.82
[14] Muir p.82

HOP POLES

One of the great images of yesterday's England is hop-picking. Together with haymaking and reaping it is one of the enduring images of the countryside, made famous by seasonal pickers from the East End of London. Those pickers still hold their memories reverentially today, of their long days in a Kent countryside of fresh air, open space and lovely warm sunshine. The days of cold rain and mud and sticky clay slipped out of their minds long ago, along with their sore hands and stained skin. These were the days of cotton pinafore dresses and headscarves, when men all wore caps and trilbies. Whole families packed up and migrated to Kent for the picking season of about three weeks, starting in early September. This was their 'holiday'.

The practice dates back to the mid 19th century at least, but the seasonal need for extra labour is recorded for more than two hundred years before that. In many places it was the Romanies who provided this seasonal workforce.

It was the same in the other prime hop growing areas of Hereford/Worcester and Surrey/Hants. For the latter, people came out from Reading and the West End of London, but it's London's Eastenders going to Kent who lodge in the national memory.

The first hop-picking machine was not introduced until 1934 but those quick to use one soon found that the hops picked by machine caused a lot more work when it came to drying. There was no rush to buy the machines and the pickers' seasonal bonus to pay for warm winter clothes, decent shoes and Christmas food continued until after the Second World War. Today the whole plant stem or bine is still cut by hand but then piled onto a trailer and taken away to a machine that strips off the fruit heads, or hops, at the rate of over a thousand bines per hour.

Hops are the fruiting heads, like little green fir cones, of the Hop plant, *Humulus lupulus*. The fruit heads[1] are rich in tannins that are exploited as flavouring and preservative in the brewing of beer. Indeed without hops beer wouldn't be beer - it would be ale, although today the word beer is used generically to cover all beers, ales and porters. The plant is native to Britain, arriving soon after the last Ice Age.[2] It is a herbaceous climber, sending up its bines to six metres or more and therefore needs support - long, straight poles, like those of the coppiced Chestnut.

---

[1] called *strobuli*
[2] Godwin p.242

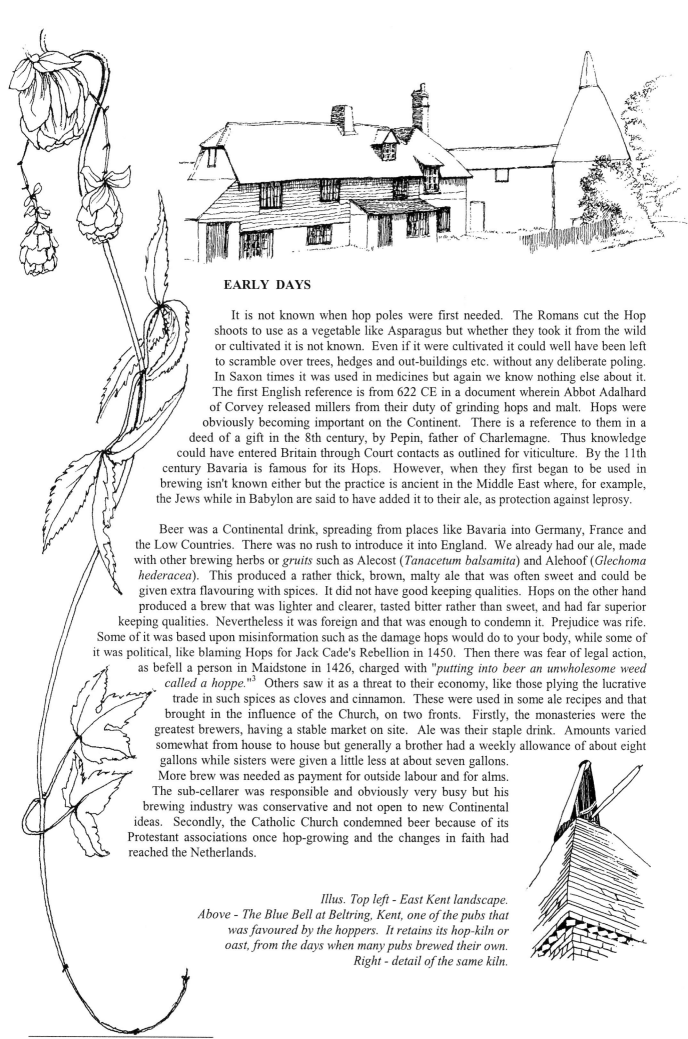

EARLY DAYS

It is not known when hop poles were first needed. The Romans cut the Hop shoots to use as a vegetable like Asparagus but whether they took it from the wild or cultivated it is not known. Even if it were cultivated it could well have been left to scramble over trees, hedges and out-buildings etc. without any deliberate poling. In Saxon times it was used in medicines but again we know nothing else about it. The first English reference is from 622 CE in a document wherein Abbot Adalhard of Corvey released millers from their duty of grinding hops and malt. Hops were obviously becoming important on the Continent. There is a reference to them in a deed of a gift in the 8th century, by Pepin, father of Charlemagne. Thus knowledge could have entered Britain through Court contacts as outlined for viticulture. By the 11th century Bavaria is famous for its Hops. However, when they first began to be used in brewing isn't known either but the practice is ancient in the Middle East where, for example, the Jews while in Babylon are said to have added it to their ale, as protection against leprosy.

Beer was a Continental drink, spreading from places like Bavaria into Germany, France and the Low Countries. There was no rush to introduce it into England. We already had our ale, made with other brewing herbs or *gruits* such as Alecost (*Tanacetum balsamita*) and Alehoof (*Glechoma hederacea*). This produced a rather thick, brown, malty ale that was often sweet and could be given extra flavouring with spices. It did not have good keeping qualities. Hops on the other hand produced a brew that was lighter and clearer, tasted bitter rather than sweet, and had far superior keeping qualities. Nevertheless it was foreign and that was enough to condemn it. Prejudice was rife. Some of it was based upon misinformation such as the damage hops would do to your body, while some of it was political, like blaming Hops for Jack Cade's Rebellion in 1450. Then there was fear of legal action, as befell a person in Maidstone in 1426, charged with "*putting into beer an unwholesome weed called a hoppe.*"[3] Others saw it as a threat to their economy, like those plying the lucrative trade in such spices as cloves and cinnamon. These were used in some ale recipes and that brought in the influence of the Church, on two fronts. Firstly, the monasteries were the greatest brewers, having a stable market on site. Ale was their staple drink. Amounts varied somewhat from house to house but generally a brother had a weekly allowance of about eight gallons while sisters were given a little less at about seven gallons. More brew was needed as payment for outside labour and for alms. The sub-cellarer was responsible and obviously very busy but his brewing industry was conservative and not open to new Continental ideas. Secondly, the Catholic Church condemned beer because of its Protestant associations once hop-growing and the changes in faith had reached the Netherlands.

Illus. Top left - East Kent landscape.
Above - The Blue Bell at Beltring, Kent, one of the pubs that was favoured by the hoppers. It retains its hop-kiln or oast, from the days when many pubs brewed their own.
Right - detail of the same kiln.

[3] Filmer p.7

Despite all this, beer crossed the sea from the Low Countries and gained a foothold in England, but when? *"It is generally believed that beer first arrived in England in 1400, at Winchelsea harbour in East Sussex, in a consignment ordered by Dutch merchants working in England."*[4] This is very precise. It sounds a little too precise when there was so much traffic between England and the Continent. So there may well be truth in the claim that beer was popularised gradually by Flemish immigrant weavers in the reign of Edward III (r.1327-77). Archaeologists find tantalising bits of evidence that might push the date back much farther. Godwin[5] for example, cites the wooden boat excavated out of Graveney Marsh in Kent that was found to contain 'considerable numbers' of hops, which were interpreted as the cargo. When the timbers were radio-carbon dated they were found to be 1080 BP. Were the hops for brewing and if so, were they for beer or for mixing with other gruits to make ale? What is certain is that the Dutch-speaking peoples played a significant role. The evidence is in the dictionary. We adopted their units of measurement into our language: the 18 gallon *kilderkin* and the 9 gallon *firkin*. Why we chose to do this rather than measure and trade in our own units is an interesting point. Perhaps it was for convenience of taxation. If tolls and other dues were set already on these foreign measurements it would have been easier to continue in this way.

---

[4] Filmer p.7
[5] Godwin p.242

Early records don't necessarily tell us all we want to know, since references to beer rarely specify whether it was imported or home-brewed. We do know that England was importing large amounts of hops, before we grew our own. The prime source of imported hops was the Netherlands. Certainly hops in beer became a familiar option through the 1400s. In particular, they won favour with the lay brewers who did not have the guaranteed on-site market of the monasteries. Beer kept longer and was therefore more versatile. Also, they found they needed fewer hops for beer than they did other gruits for ale. This brought the costs down and helped to compensate for transport charges. McLean states all the big London breweries were using them by 1464. So when did we start growing our own?

These aspects of our social history feature in the numerous breweries and storage undercrofts among many of our monastic ruins. The *illustration* is of Bayham Abbey, which straddles the border between Kent and Sussex.[10] Here visitors will find not only impressive ruins but also the rest of the ground plan laid bare, making it easier to understand. There are two cellars: one older than the other. If you inspect the stonework of the main access doorway to the newer undercroft (*illus. inset*) you can see that it had to be widened. It is thought this must have been to allow passage of a larger size of cask. It won't have been for the firkin or kilderkin as these are small. That was important for beer because once a cask was opened the contents had to be used quickly due to its limited keeping qualities. The casks for wine might interest us more since French ones could well have been made of Chestnut.

*Illustrations of
Bayham Abbey
sketched and reproduced by
kind permission of
English Heritage.*

[6] listed most often as East Sussex but researchers need to review both counties. It's social history relates decidedly to Kent.

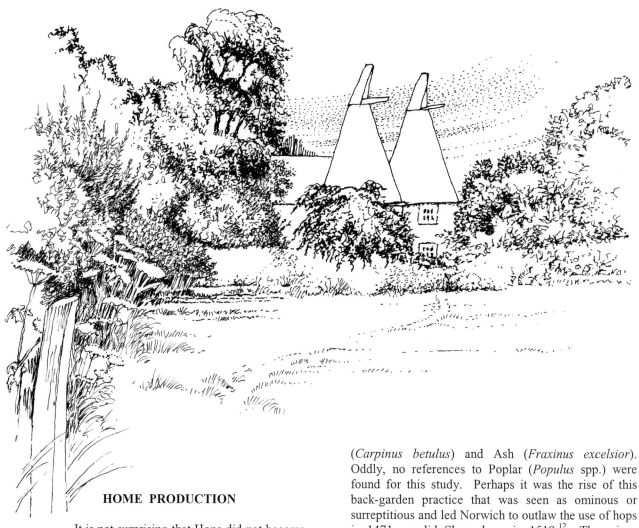

HOME PRODUCTION

It is not surprising that Hops did not become common in the *early* Middle Ages when so much of the potential prime growing areas was being worked in strips in the open field system. The best arable land was needed for the production of corn, beans and peas etc. to sustain the manorial community. To take some of that land for Hops in the hope that the return would compensate adequately was a risky decision. Thus it is not until later in the Middle Ages that opportunities arose for changing the cropping regime as the earlier open field system evolved gradually into the private ownership and hired labour system that is familiar today.

"Tradition has it that the first English hop garden was created in the parish of Westbere near Canterbury in 1520 although there is a counter claim for a site at Little Chart, near Ashford, also in Kent."[11] This might be only part of the picture because alongside the specialist breweries there were the alewives brewing for home consumption; every farmer's wife was expected to be just as competent at brewing as she was at baking bread. Thus Hops became familiar in back gardens and remained there for several hundred years. It is probably for these back-garden plots that early references to the poles apply, since they include such unlikely trees as Maple (*Acer campestre*), Sallow (*Salix caprea* et al) and even Yew (*Taxus baccata*), together with more likely contenders as Hornbeam

(*Carpinus betulus*) and Ash (*Fraxinus excelsior*). Oddly, no references to Poplar (*Populus* spp.) were found for this study. Perhaps it was the rise of this back-garden practice that was seen as ominous or surreptitious and led Norwich to outlaw the use of hops in 1471, as did Shrewsbury in 1519.[12] There is a tradition that Parliament itself was petitioned to ban it in 1440. Despite the attempts at suppression, Hops started to become commonplace as a field crop in the early 1500s. Then the whole system changed, when Henry VIII dissolved the monasteries, in the late 1530s. That took out the main conservative element favouring ale, removed the breweries altogether and so opened up a greater market for lay brewers, together with the need for new premises to replace all the lost monastic guesthouses. The response to this seems to have been rapid. Today, the oldest survivor of these lay breweries is Young's Ram Brewery in Wandsworth, London, dating from Elizabethan times.

FIRST MANUAL PUBLISHED

The Hop won through all the political vicissitudes so that from Tudor times there were manuals in English to instruct landowners in the production of this crop. The first came in 1574 as *A Perfite Platform of a Hoppe Garden* by Reynolde Scot. He grew Hops himself, at Brabourne and Smeeth in Kent so he knew what he was talking about and produced an ideal handbook. It was authoritative, succinct and each stage of the instructions was illustrated with beautiful clear woodcuts. It was so popular it had to be reprinted within two years and then a third time in another two years.

---

[7] Filmer p.8

[8] Filmer p.7

How amazed villagers must have been when the first field was turned over to Hops. They must have gone out specially to have a look, since they'd heard people were making rows of 'molehills' all across the land. Row upon row of hills was scooped up out of the topsoil to knee height and into the top of these were planted the Hop sets. Then as soon as the shoots appeared in the spring, Scot instructed the growers to insert the poles, at the rate of three or four poles per planting group. They were tilted outwards slightly so that the bines would hang free from the top and not entangle so much and also to funnel out warm moist air that would otherwise encourage mildew. As the season progressed, weeds were scoured up with a sort of mattock and the spoil added to the hills, till they were some three feet high. That was reduced to half the height during the 17th century and has now disappeared altogether, although people still refer to the planting sites as hills.

Scot instructed that the poles be placed 2-3 inches away from the plant and be sunk 12-18 inches into the ground. In size the poles should be 9-10 inches round at the base and some 15-16 feet high. That way the Hop outgrew the top and hung down, promoting it to flower and fruit. Height varied according to the cultivar, the season and the soil fertility. A shrewd countryman could judge the fertility of a field by the height of the hop poles - 10, 12 or 18 feet. First season plants only needed the broken tops off old poles.[3] The huge demand for poles was not just to set up the fields in the first place but was ongoing. In Scot 's experience an acre of Hops would need about 300 replacement poles per year. Each would last 6-7 years if looked after with care. That means, not leaving them in a heap on the ground all winter to trap rain and rot. Degraded and broken poles were not wasted but went to the colliers for turning into charcoal to fuel the drying kilns.

Scot did not promote Chestnut poles. His book specifies another coppiced tree, Alder (*Alnus glutinosa*). The poles were to be felled in the winter, when there was least sap in them, specifically between "Allhallowentyde and Christmas." The poles should be clean of "*scrags or knobbles*" which was sound advice since it makes it easier to remove the bines. He also reported that "*Hops seem more willinglye and naturalle to encline to alders than any other kind of pole.*" That said, people soon recognised the superior qualities of Chestnut poles and those were well established by the time of Marshall's *Rural Economy of the Southern Counties* in 1798. The changeover to Chestnut appears to have been largely complete by about 1800, despite the first duty to be levied having arrived in 1710, when other bitters were excluded.

His choice may well reflect availability on a large scale for field cropping since Chestnut coppices were not general. As far as we know most coppices being used were of medieval origin and would have included

a mixture of species to suit the varying needs of the manor. Increasingly, and in the south-east in particular, any failed stool that needed replacing was likely to be replaced by a Chestnut if the soil suited. There were thousands of acres of suitable soil in the south-east, not just in Kent.

All the south-eastern counties - Kent, Surrey, Sussex, Hampshire - were growing Hops on a large scale. Even marginal land was pressed into service and Chestnuts were grown too as windbreak screens between the fields themselves. It was certainly big business but everything depended upon the season. Ruin came with fungal attack such as mildew, insect attack from blight and wind attack when storms tore down the alleys. It wasn't long before country wisdom absorbed the truism that more money could be made out of Hops than any other crop but that Hops carried the greatest risks.

Make your money out of hops.
Make your ruin out of hops.

It wasn't so much the methods of growing Hops that changed through this period but the farmers. They gave up other crops in favour of Hops. There was an enormous expansion in the national acreage given over to them. By the mid 19th century they were being grown in fifty-three counties of Britain, although Scotland and Wales were soon to abandon them. English counties declined too as production became centred upon just six:

Kent	46,600 acres
Surrey	2,300 acres
Sussex	11,000 acres
Hants	3,200 acres
Herefs	6,000 acres
Worc	2,500 acres

(figures for 1878, from Parker)

The other counties had only about 500 acres between them. Of course this all required an equally dramatic expansion of Chestnut coppices to provide the poles.

HOW MUCH OF ENGLAND?

THE MID NINETEENTH CENTURY

The methods of growing Hops, as introduced into this country and promoted by people like Reynolde Scot, remained unchanged right through to the third quarter of the 19th century. During that time the prosperity of the growers funded fine timber-framed houses that still make Kent villages famous today. Some are concealed behind wall tiles, brick facades and white weatherboarding, and have been modified with dormer windows and little porches, to give that rich assemblage that makes each village unique. It satisfied that English delight in the Picturesque, and created a huge demand for reproduced images. What were once terms of appreciation have now become almost derisory; terms such as 'picture post card village', 'ye olde worlde,' 'chocolate-boxy,' and 'pretty-pretty,' thus diverting attention from the quality of the heritage - illustrated on this page with sketches made at Lamberhurst.

Just how much of England's woodland *was* given over to hop pole production? That simple question doesn't have a simple answer because there are so many variables in cropping both the Hops and the poles. For a start there is no uniformity in the density of hills per acre but is often quoted as about 1,000 to 1,200. Then the number of poles per hill varied, usually 3-4, but even that small variation makes a huge difference to the final answer of 3,000-4,800 poles per

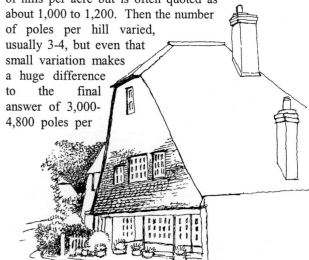

acre. Some texts quote a far lower number. Poles would soon need replacing, at the rate of 500-600 per acre per year but again far lower totals have been published.

Turning now to the coppices, the totals of stools per acre varied but for this discussion let us accept 590, yielding 2,500 poles. They were cropped at the time on a 10-12 year rotation, so this again offers widely differing results. Multiply that by the total of 71,600 acres of Hops listed for the six counties above and the range of possible totals can exceed 250 square miles. Add extra coppices to provide for the setting up of new fields and to provide materials for craftsmen working Chestnut in totally different ways and we begin to realise the significance of the Chestnut tree in the English landscape. That's particularly so when the square miles are imagined as the small woodland units so typical of rural England. It's a lot of woodland for the sake of a pint of beer!

CHANGE OF SYSTEM

Having remained basically untouched for over 400 years the system started to change about 1850-75. By then growers were treating their poles better in terms of cleaning them between seasons and applying gas tar as an extra preservative. Soon there were a number of other chemical preservatives available, such as *Kytons Patent Preparation*, but it's not known exactly what these contained. Poles were soaked in it for several days, which cost about 2d per pole.[10] That cost £5 per 600 replacement poles per acre, which was far more expensive than buying new poles. The prices of those varied enormously, from 8-30 shillings per thousand in 1840, so preservatives had to be really effective to make their use economical. Growers certainly took it on and then, by 1860, creosote came into use.

That created a severe reduction in the market for new poles, which got another set-back c.1875. That was when Henry Butcher of Sheldwich in Kent introduced the wirework system whereby Hops were grown up strings instead of poles. The strings were suspended from an overhead system of wires, supported on Chestnut poles. The number of poles required was now far fewer - only 150-200 per acre.[11] Poles needed to be longer and stouter so the coppice rotation was extended from 10-12 years to 14-16 years. The durability of the larger poles meant that a system could last twenty five years. Prices fell so much that by the end of the 19th century it was once again viable for small growers to return to training their bines up poles instead of strings, even to the extent of using untreated poles.[12] Nevertheless variants of the wire system came to prevail.

Alongside these changes there were improvements in the fruiting qualities of the Hop itself. Growers selected good strains of the plant and gave them local names, like 'Fuggles'. This led to regional variations. Thus 'Fuggles' and similar cultivars, became the prime choice of the Surrey/Hants growers, around Farnham and Alton Their brew was lighter than that of Kent and this lighter beer became fashionable in the 19th century, causing a massive expansion of production in this area. It was the basis of the wealth of the two towns at that time.

Production declined through the second half of the 20th century with the promotion of cheap foreign holidays giving consumers an enthusiasm for Continental wines and lagers. Back home this led to the Campaign for Real Ale (CAMRA) that not only affected consumerism but also led to a demand for the continued use of traditional strains of Hops such as 'Fuggles'. This strain was formerly used for 80% of English beer but the plant was not disease resistant and nearly died out. Reviving it, with a grant from the then Common Market saved valuable genetic material for the continued development of better cultivars. That work has been pioneered at the Wye College of Agriculture at Brook in Kent, which since 1947, has had a special department devoted to Hops that is now recognised as a world authority. Developing 'better' Hops has included those with a higher tannin content in their fruits so that fewer hops are needed and therefore fewer hectares producing them. That has been achieved and the land use in 2000 was down to 1,974.49 hectares. Even worse news for the coppice workers is that these new developments include dwarf hops!

[10] Griffin p.26
[11] Griffin p.68
[12] Griffin p.27

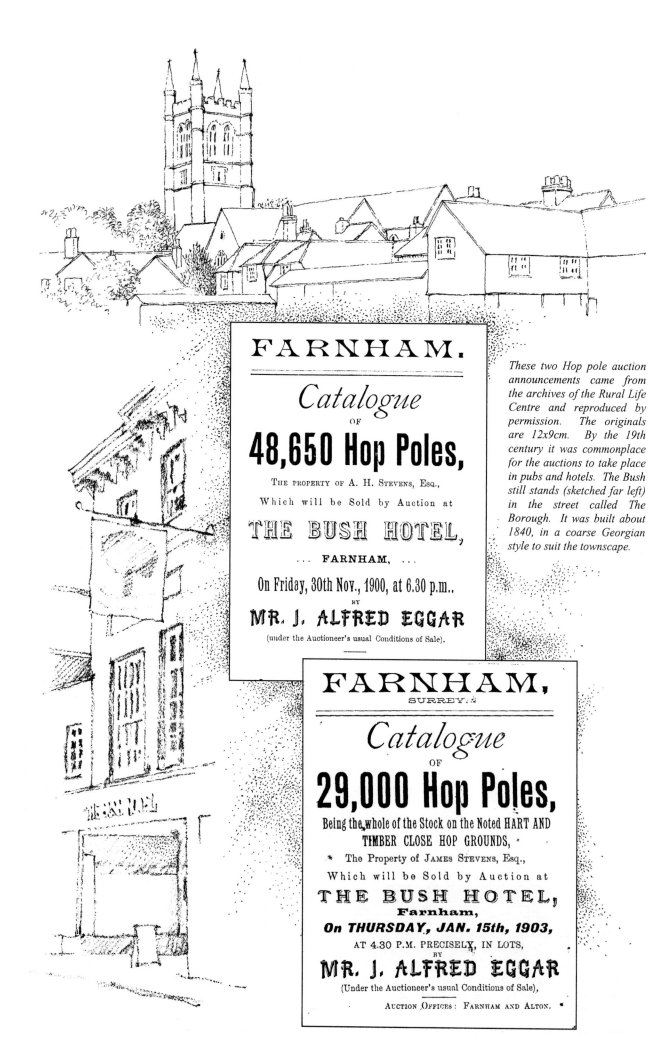

FARNHAM.

Catalogue

OF

48,650 Hop Poles,

THE PROPERTY OF A. H. STEVENS, ESQ.,

Which will be Sold by Auction at

THE BUSH HOTEL,

... FARNHAM, ...

On Friday, 30th Nov., 1900, at 6.30 p.m..

BY

MR. J. ALFRED EGGAR

(under the Auctioneer's usual Conditions of Sale).

These two Hop pole auction announcements came from the archives of the Rural Life Centre and reproduced by permission. The originals are 12x9cm. By the 19th century it was commonplace for the auctions to take place in pubs and hotels. The Bush still stands (sketched far left) in the street called The Borough. It was built about 1840, in a coarse Georgian style to suit the townscape.

FARNHAM,

SURREY.

Catalogue

OF

29,000 Hop Poles,

Being the whole of the Stock on the Noted HART AND TIMBER CLOSE HOP GROUNDS,

The Property of JAMES STEVENS, Esq.,

Which will be Sold by Auction at

THE BUSH HOTEL,

Farnham,

On THURSDAY, JAN. 15th, 1903,

AT 4.30 P.M. PRECISELY, IN LOTS,

BY

MR. J. ALFRED EGGAR

(Under the Auctioneer's usual Conditions of Sale),

AUCTION OFFICES: FARNHAM AND ALTON.

Farnham's agricultural history, which gave rise to the wealth of the town, is illustrated on two concrete bas-relief panels on the wall of the police station in Downing Street. Sketched above is the top of one showing, from left to right, the hop kilns, then the stilt walkers tying the strings, then the wire system and strings, ending far right with the bines up the strings.

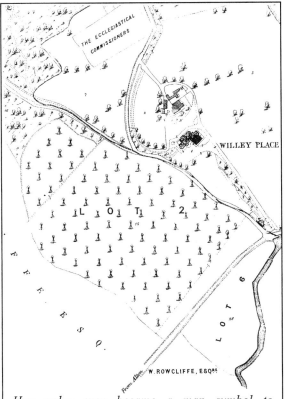

Hop poles even became a map symbol to designate which fields were devoted to the crop, as in this example from lands just beyond Farnham, into Hampshire. It has been lifted from an estate map in the archives of the Rural Life Centre, and reproduced with their co-operation. Boxed right is an enlargement. Presumably the loop over the top of the poles represents the head of bine growth.

The bines sketched above are carved in stone in the nearby parish church at Shackleford. The church dates from 1865 and was designed by the prominent architect Sir Giles Gilbert Scott. When it came to the sculptures the children of the village school were asked to bring examples of the local plants to be carved. In all they brought forty-three, including the hops, which were carved twice. The piece sketched here is on a capital of the north aisle arcade. It has a curious error. To the right of the two lower strobili is the unmistakable coiled tendril of the White Bryony plant. Somebody got in a muddle!
Reproduced by permission of the church warden.

WINTER WORK

The enduring images of hop production are of the early autumn picking and most of those are for Kent. Elsewhere the scenes were similar. We can visit the Hop country of the Hampshire/Surrey borderlands courtesy of the writings of the Farnham wheelwright, George Sturt. His descriptions of his local childhood in the 1860s give a more balanced view since they include winter scenes and work, and the following two paragraphs are taken from his autobiography, which has a whole chapter devoted to Hops.

"The poles (the spile[13] having been sorted out of them) were piled up into 'aisles,' and looked like tents all across the hop-ground. There they stood throughout the winter, restoring to the ground a look of order. It was needed. For indeed all was untidy and desolate when first the hops were down. It seemed as if winter had come; and it was a common remark that the cold had been let in upon Farnham town. Certainly the wide hop-ground everywhere looked bleak and desolate. The soil had been trodden flat by the pickers; here and there a solitary pole, left standing for some reason, stood gaunt and naked to the weather. Occasionally a rook would settle atop of the pole; or occasionally a battered tin can would be put there. Yet the untidy hop-grounds made a fine playground for boys; one felt it a proud thing, too, to climb one of the hop-poles."

"Another thing too marked the winter. New poles to replace the spile, were carted into the hop-ground, and had to be pointed there. I suppose this was for the hop-ground man to do. With one hand the man held the pole on a block a little lower than his knee, with the other hand he swung down on the pole a light axe. And the axe must have been sharp, and the hand that swung it strong, for five or six chops pointed the pole. I was too little to know or care much about this work, though I like very well to see a man at it, so deft, so industrious. With his trousers strapped or tied under the knees, and with a short pipe in his mouth, the man always looked good-tempered. Why not? It was probably not too well paid a job - piece-work, and with the chips as a perquisite; but it was out-o'-doors; and with every blow of the axe a gratified sensation would run up the man's arm - the sensation of a touch from the outside world that is not one's-self." [14]
(On the fields too the poles were stripped of their bark.)

Sturt moved out of Farnham to the neighbouring village of The Bourne where he adopted the pseudonym 'George Bourne' and under that published the memories of his gardener, whom he called 'Fred Bettesworth'. Really he was Fred Grover, and thanks to the detective work of Michael Leishman, the code of pseudonyms for people and places, has been

deciphered and so we can visit the locations again today. Thus Mr. Leisham was able to report that "Penstead" in the extract following[15] was in fact Binstead and there we met him on a cold winter's afternoon to explore the locations that he'd identified for us from the documents in the Hampshire Record Office. Sturt had recorded enough detail to make that possible. On the way we passed the stark winter field illustrated above (the overhead wire system had not been developed at the time of the following incident). The first dandelion flowers were promising springtime, as were drapes of aubrieta on the stone walls but there could be no celebration in winter with a rich dark heartening ploughsoil in the fields around. Instead, the soil looks cold and anaemic from where the plough has shared up the underlying chalk to the surface. The wide views from the ridge across to the Downs made you cry with cold wind. It was from here one winter's day that Fred Bettesworth set off to the Chestnut coppices to bring back a load of Hop poles:-

---

[13] 'spile' = local dialect for spoil - broken and rotten poles.
[14] Sturt; *Small Boy*; p.82-3

[15] from ch.3, *Bettesworth Book*

40

"The young man had left farmer Barnes and Penstead, and was working - as carter still - for a brother of the farmer, 'Old Jimmy Barnes.' One cold day, when the weather was between snowing and raining and freezing, young Bettesworth, carting hop-poles for Mr. Barnes, found his work too heartbreaking to be endured. He was miles from home. The tracks through the coppice - you could not call them roads - were knee-deep in mud. There were two horses for the solitary young man to manage, and of course a two-horse load of poles to be got home on the long pole-carriage. Wherefore it happened that the heavily-loaded 'carriage' stuck fast in deep clay, upon which it behoved Bettesworth to unload, get horses and pole-carriage out of the hole they had sunk in, and then replace the load. Once, or twice even, this might have been borne, but six times it happened - six times he had to unload and reload those icy poles, snow and rain whirling through the coppice all the time, mud begriming him, his beloved horses suffering, his own hands chapped and raw from handling the half-frozen poles. Long after dark he got home tired out; but there were the horses to see to. He made them comfortable: got to rest himself about midnight."

Readers may not be surprised to hear that the next day he walked out on his job. It's his age that is surprising. Michael Leishman has identified 'farmer Barnes' as Andrews who farmed from East Court. When this information, and other details in the books, is compared with documents in the Hampshire Record Office (Winchester) we learn that *Bettesworth* was aged thirteen - give or take a few months either way. Boys started work after the age of eight in many cases and were expected to learn the skills of stable and field to become a carter or ploughboy by the age of twelve. So sending a thirteen-year-old out for poles with a two-horse team and wagon would not have been unusual. It's just that we don't expect that of our young teens today.

There's a hint of this youthfulness in the next memoir of the book, when Bettesworth, having walked out on the job, goes to London and stopped for the night at Staines, where he tried to get a job as a carter. *Now* we can appreciate the doubt in the mind of his prospective employer when he points at two of the largest horses Fred had ever seen and asks, "D'ye think you could drive they two 'orses?" Fred said he could, but secretly had his doubts. Next day he drove them, fully laden, through all the London horse-traffic, right into Smithfield. So he stayed with that job for three years.

The village of Binstead is still much as it was when the young Fred Grover knew it. The lane takes right-angled turns round the churchyard, passing old houses at each turn. The whattle and daub panels used to infill between the timbers have long since been replaced by warm Hampshire brick in the example left.

Chestnut Paling Fencing

TIMES OF CHANGE

When Hop growers changed their support system from individual poles to the overhead wire system there was a dramatic drop in the demand for Hop poles. This was grave economic news for both the landowners of Chestnut coppices and the coppice workers alike. Salvation came in the form of a new type of fencing that was soon in popular demand. It required the same Chestnut poles, the same coppice skills and the same tools.[1] Only the end product and its marketing changed. The hoopers were the first to convert to pale-making, then the spile-makers and lastly the hurdlers.. Today fencing is still an important use for Chestnut.

COPPICING FOR FENCING

In order to appreciate a Chestnut coppice landscape from the viewpoint of the fence-maker we were helped by Stephen Homewood, of *J. E. Homewood* & Son at Haslemere. Through the midday glare of a blazing July day he led the way up narrow Surrey lanes into the hills to a 16 acre site. It's cropped for his family fencing business, started by his father in 1946.

The 15 year old crop either side of the ride had closed its canopy overhead to make a dark tunnel from the gate to the cants[2] ahead that had been cut the previous winter. Their recovery rate was impressive. Already their growth was 3-4 ft high, but they had got off to a good start since there had been several weeks without rain in the spring. This suits Chestnuts fine. It's just like their original homelands - so the buds burst early. There were expectations that late frosts in May would burn off the soft growth but it turned wet instead. Chestnut growth slows down when the soil is wet but the sandstone hills had drained rapidly and the stools had flourished into great hummocks of greenery.

Usually an abundance of buds burst from the cut stools, numbering anything from 50-150 depending upon the stool age and size. These fight for the light, with many failing, so that they become self-thinning, without the expensive demand of human labour. The strongest shoots forge ahead and this was clear to see. The longest leaders soon outreach the browsing height of the deer, which is good news for the grower. On

this particular day a Roe Deer and her fawn moved deeper into the woodland as we passed along the ride. Even a dainty deer makes a clatter on Chestnut leaves; there's nothing discreet about Chestnuts!

Thus the stools decide naturally how many poles they will bear eventually. This varies enormously from stool to stool and any notions of thinning them to a uniform number is not part of Chestnut coppice practice. Across the ride were cants in their 15th year and the poles varied from 2-3 on small stools up to 8 or more on the larger stools. Despite being the same age, there was considerable variation in the size of stool, even under the same conditions in the same cant, revealing probable genetic variation. Dotted over the hilltop were 'standards' - mature Oak and Chestnut trees that shelter the regenerating stools. Root competition from these was retarding a ring of stools around them but even so, there were still some stools doing far better than others. All the shoots though were spreading their broad glossy leaves in the hot July sun to maximise the energy source. Nothing crops better on these dry, sandy, infertile soils.

A 20-year-old section had shot up to some 30 ft. and was flowering heavily. They were being left a few more years till the majority of big poles were some 28-30 inches in girth. Then they are serviceable for post-and-rail fencing. This is fashionable again where landowners want a traditional 'natural' look, and is also used around car parks etc. on country properties 'open to the public'. Otherwise, for chestnut paling fencing, the stools are cropped when the usable poles are about 6 inches in diameter. Each of those poles will then yield:-

    one 6 ft section for cleaving into 10 pales
    one 4 ft section for cleaving into 8 pales
    one or two 4 ft sections for cleaving into 6 pales
    leaving enough for one post out of the top.

Cutting takes place from about 25th October through to March. The processing, from poles to finished pales, is all performed on the woodland site, by the pale-maker. The poles are stripped of their bark,

---

[1] although the traditional adze was superseded by the break axe (Porter)

[2] cants are working units of a woodland, ranging usually from half to three acres

either by hand, with a drawknife, or more usually nowadays, by a bark-stripping machine. Then they are riven by hand, working with the grain radially, which automatically produces the familiar triangular shape in section. Then they are roughly pointed, traditionally with a billhook but more likely nowadays by poking the end into the bark-stripping machine and giving it a deft little twist. Finally they are trimmed to uniform length (only half an inch variation granted) and tied in bundles of twenty-five. Nowadays they are tied with binder twine because it is strong, durable and readily available. The crucial point is to tie the bundle top and bottom so tight that the bundles do not fall apart during rough handling. That is achieved with a traditional technique that must be very ancient. Two lengths of twine are stretched on the ground the right distance apart and the pales are stacked on top. Then the bundle is compressed tight with 'packers' - a length of twine with wooden handles that is looped under the pales, drawn up over it and crossed, so that when the handles are stretched outwards the loop hugs the pales up tighter together. Then for the crucial tightness one end of each handle is forced against the ground as the top ends are pushed outwards. It's all a matter of leverage. It's quicker and easier to loop the packers round if the pales are a bit above the ground and so they are laid in two cradles. On this site the cradles were made out of the handles of two old galvanised buckets - waste not want not!

The processing from tree to pales takes place entirely in the coppices, with shelter provided by a 'bender'. These were originally made entirely of coppice products. Then tarpaulins became available but nowadays a plastic sheet is used.

The bundles are then transported back to the yard and stacked to dry, ready to be wired. There's a machine to do that, stretching the galvanised wires tight for the pales to be inserted by hand and then it twists the wires to hold the pale at the correct spacing. Pales are wired top and bottom and for the taller grades a third central wiring is added. The spacing between pales can be adjusted from near touching to 1.5, 2, 3, 4 or 5 inches. Recently there has been a demand for 10 inches for a special fencing used in the conservation of the capercaillie.

Chestnut pales are extremely strong and durable, making a fence that is long lasting and therefore a good investment. The Chestnut Fencing Manufacturers' Society says it will "last up to twenty years or more" and I can remember one being in place fifty years ago and it's still there now, albeit with several pales missing. I don't suppose it would withstand being climbed over but it certainly hasn't decayed away nor needed replacing as a boundary marker. It's not the fencing that lets you down so much as the supporting posts, which will eventually rot off in the ground. So long as these are inspected from time to time and

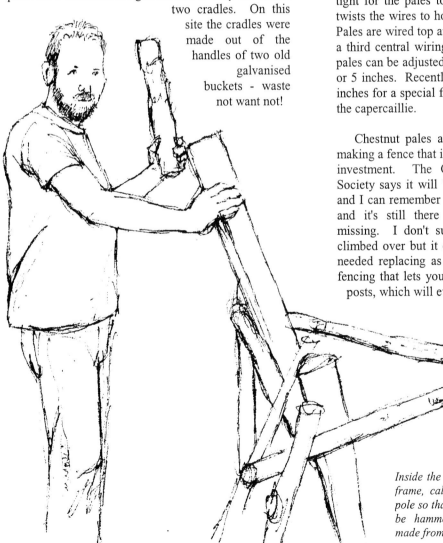

Inside the bender a rustic triangular frame, called a brake, supports the pole so that the adze (not shown) can be hammered in using a 'mallet' made from a length of pole.

replaced if needs be then the product is far more durable than other types of wooden fencing. Good Chestnut posts should always be used. The product is so fine, and submits to standardisation, that it carries a British Standard, specifically *BS 1722 Part 4 Cleft Chestnut Pale Fencing.*

Statements that this product stimulated the planting of Chestnut coppices around 1800 do not stand up to scrutiny. The essential characteristic of the product is the galvanised wire that holds the pales and the process of 'hot-dip galvanising' was not patented until 1837 (by the French engineer, Sorel). The technique was introduced into Britain in 1843, according to a reference in the catalogue of the Great Exhibition in 1851. The planting up of new coppices was in response

The triangular shape of the brake enables the pole to be manoeuvred to any angle to enable the adze to follow the grain as the pales are cleft from the pole.

to the increasing demand for Hop poles, not fencing. It was the decline in demand for Hop poles at the end of the 19th century that founded the fence-making as an alternative use for the raw material. The fencing technique is believed to have been introduced from France, some say from Brittany, by the end of the 19th century. The prime area for the development of the British industry was the western Weald, where the Chestnut grows well on the sandstone hills of South West Surrey and North West Sussex.[3]

Through the first half of the 20th century the industry flourished. Never before had there been anything quite so flexible in long lengths, which could be rolled up, to ease some transport problems, and then unrolled around any shape of site, adapting to corners and curves and even changes in gradient or level. With its natural, somewhat rustic, appearance it was much used on country estates. Its close paling was a great advantage over post-and-rail where small livestock were concerned. Barbed wired was available by this time[4] but was yet to become universal. However, there was competition from the iron and steel industry that was mass-producing a metal version of post-and-rail to undercut the cost of the traditional oak version. That

drew the invective of influential writers such as Gertrude Jekyll:- *"It is often a matter of surprise and regret to me, when I see in large places, with hundreds of acres of woodland, what appears to be a thoughtless and stupid use of iron railings. These unsightly fencings are wilfully brought into what is perhaps the most beautiful landscape, and always with disastrous effect, while the material for the most suitable fencing [oak] is close at hand and wasted. It is usually urged in the defence of the iron railing that it is permanent, whereas some day the oak fence must be renewed. But it should be remembered that the labour of the not unfrequent painting with black tar-varnish - perhaps the ugliest covering the wretched things could have - is also a permanent charge."[5]*

Writing from South West Surrey, she was in a heartland of traditional country skills, where oak fencing still prevailed - but not exclusively. Perhaps her invective was directed in part at her neighbour in Witley Park who had miles of the new metal version. She doesn't mention Chestnut fencing; despite living in a prime growing area (the coppice described earlier in this chapter is within easy walking distance of her home). Perhaps it was too new, but not so far away, at Haslemere, Sir Robert Hunter, co-founder of the National Trust, is believed to have used chestnut paling on his Meadfield estate.

---

[3] There was some competition for the material from the walking stick makers who established themselves in South West Surrey, in the second half of the 19th century. The most important factory was at Wormley, with its own coppices; rivals drew upon other coppices in the area.

[4] first patent taken out 25th June 1867 by Lucien Smith of Ohio

---

[5] Jekyll pp.25-8

The second major outlet, for decades, was the construction industry, to fence off civil engineering and building sites. It may not look much of a safeguard to keep people from climbing over but the pales are too closely set to allow a foot onto the top wire. They are certainly not for sitting on to swing a leg over, even though they are only pointed bluntly. An intruder slips only once! Rarely is the fencing stretched and posted so very tightly that there isn't enough slack to allow it to wobble, quite vigorously, under an intruder's weight. That soon dumps them back from whence they came. After decades of this prime usage coloured plastic strips were promoted for such sites. They were even more flexible and much cheaper - but they only warn. They are no deterrent in themselves. Nevertheless, this use of plastic has reduced severely the commercial outlets available to the fence-maker. It has thus hastened the decline of coppicing and the rural economy. The plastic is not a renewable resource, unlike Chestnut and neither is it recycled. It does not have the aesthetic qualities of Chestnut either. Indeed most people think it is an eyesore - cheap and nasty.

The third major outlet was to Local Authorities. They ran it alongside footpaths, round car parks, clay pits and everywhere else over which they had a duty to ensure public safety. Even more importantly, they chose it to fence off gardens in public sector housing estates. That lasted until superseded by chain link fencing (from c.1936) which soon became first choice with many Councils. After the Second World War increasing wealth led to an expansion of private sector housing which lowered the status of chestnut paling fence, since it was associated with building sites and council estates. Private housing schemes certainly didn't want it and soon they were to dispense with fencing altogether, as open-plan developments became fashionable (and cheaper). That said, even in the early days there was never a phase of popularity in private housing for the chestnut paling. Nobody influential promoted it. Despite major movements in garden style from the 1880s onwards,[6] alongside the development of suburbia, the emphasis was upon the garden itself, not its boundary. Privacy was crucial. The new

suburbanites wanted their own little enclosed space and so panel fencing was employed: *"The back garden, which might be 24 to 60m (80 to 200 feet) long, was often carefully screened by high weather-boarding fencing from the neighbours."[7]* The reverse was true of the front garden where it was important, socially, that everybody could see it. Builders of new developments often initiated this by sponsoring front garden competitions with their first-time buyers (so as to get their developments looking as attractive as possible as quickly as possible). The manicured formal designs lay behind a formal front boundary - low wall, iron railing, neatly clipped hedge or a rigid picket fence but not a chestnut paling fence. It just didn't have the right ambience! Today, the revival of so many of those styles is still excluding this fencing. The all-influential Chelsea Flower Show displays plenty of rustic furniture and picket fencing but the potential of chestnut paling is still being ignored. It has amazing potential for supporting climbing plants, since popular climbers, like honeysuckle and clematis, flower when they reach the upper limit of their supports but run them along the top of chestnut paling fencing to enjoy blooms and scents close-up.

Finally, out on the coppice site, the pales are stacked ready for transporting back to the yard where they are fed into the machine that twists the galvanised wire around them. The 30 yard rolls are then ready for sale.

---

[6] see Barrett and Phillips ch.5

[7] Barrett and Phillips p.185

CAPERCAILLIE CONSERVATION

The capercaillie is the biggest grouse in the world; the male reaches three feet from tail tip to beak tip. You'll need to go to the Scottish pine forests to see it but even there you'll need luck or a good guide, for not only is it a quiet, shy and elusive bird but it is also rare. There are thought to be less than a thousand left. Thus it is it is listed on Annex 1 of the EC's Birds Directive, making it eligible for special funding towards its conservation. There is such demand for that funding from all over Europe that only about a third of applications are successful. The capercaillie is one of them. The EC has agreed to provide £2.41 million with the rest coming from the British Government and its organisations, including the Scottish Executive, Scottish Natural Heritage, the Forestry Commission and Forest Enterprise, plus contributions from charities such as the RSPB. Co-operatively this amasses the £4.82 million needed and thus we are able to fulfil our obligations under the EC for taking action to safeguard both rare species and certain habitats. The action plan is to increase capercaillie numbers to 5,000 by 2010. Attention is being focused upon eight Special Protection Areas and thirty seven other key sites, involving the co-operation of over thirty private landowners.

One of the factors identified as contributing to the capercaillie's decline is the loss of birds from flying to their death in deer fencing. They hit the upper levels of the high fencing as they take off or land and so various stratagems have been explored to try and make this fencing more visible. This is where chestnut paling comes in. They've tried putting it full-height (1.8m) up against the deer fencing and they've also tried adding it half-length (1m) as a band all along the upper level. It soon weathers to a natural grey that is far more acceptable in the landscape than orange plastic netting (which has been tested also and rejected) but at the same time it is still very visible to the birds. They've even tried it with the pales (which they call 'droppers') set at 45-60 degrees, which is certainly very noticeable against tree trunks beyond. The advantage of using palings is their thickness. When viewed from an angle the spaces appear smaller, until at the most oblique angle the fencing looks solid and diverts the birds. It's not without its problems though. One is wind resistance and another is the weight of the elevated option. It was thought both might be overcome if the spacing between the pales were increased. Thus *S. J. Homewood*, in far away Surrey, redesigned part of their machine to allow for ten inch spacing and soon the new product was journeying to Balmoral.

(Main source of inf. Scottish Executive)

OFF TO WAR

"There!" exclaimed the war veteran, pointing in his photo album to a picture of him on top of a tank in the 1940s. Behind him were perched two rolls of chestnut paling fencing. These were to be thrown down into anti-tank ditches to enable the tanks to run over the top. Such rolls of fencing had also been taken by advance landing parties to roll out over the Normandy beaches to enable the following troops and their vehicles to run over them without getting bogged down in the sands. They can be seen in the background of some published photos of General Eisenhower at the landings. More fencing was run out over muddy tracks for the same reason. Again and again the War Department had found uses for the paling fencing, known as WDTrackway - about 1,700 miles was used. They "*were in no small measure responsible for the speed of our advances of our armies after the break out from the Normandy bridgehead.*"

Twenty eight companies in Britain were working frantically to make enough, so there was no surplus fencing for home usage. We had been using some 30-40 million pales a year so the diversion to the war effort was noticeable and prices for home use rocketed 75%. The War Department contracts created a particularly heavy demand for pales since the contracts specified that the spacing between them should be no more than 1.25 inches. Thus the Home Timber Production Dept. had to help out. It bought and worked over 700 acres of Chestnut coppice and in the first year supplied 8.5 million pales. Of the contracted companies, one was 'Astolat' at Peasmarsh, near Guildford. The company was founded in 1926 by the Betteridge family but they had been fence-making since its introduction. In the early days the production was in the hands of teams of sixteen boys with a 'boss-boy' who supervised and maintained the flow of materials. Each week they would fight to have that job for the next week! Come the Second World War they were working flat-out making miles and miles of it. They sounded a little peeved that the Land Army girl they were sent could beat the lot of them! Day after day the thirty-yard rolls were taken off to the nearby Godalming Goods Station. The stacks towered twenty five feet high. These were loaded on to special trains sent by the War Department. Not all these loads were shipped abroad. Some were used for the fortification of South East England against an enemy invasion. Towards this end "*the Ministry of Supply Contracts Branch arranged for and got delivery from the fencing companies of over 3 million square yards of cleft chestnut fencing in heights varying 3-6 ft.*"

Chestnut provided for other wartime contingencies too. Poles were set up on possible landing sites for enemy aircraft to cause obstruction while other poles supported a temporary lighting system to guide in British bombers after dark and reduce the heavy casualties. A third pole system was deployed by the army as telegraph poles. *(Info. Muir, House and Porter)*

"Another interesting item was the dan buoy, a pole 17 ft long with a 2in top and 31/2 - 4in base, about the centre of which was affixed an airtight barrel or canister, while a ferrule was fixed at the top to take a lamp or flag, and at the bottom a heel fitting, to which was attached a chain and sinker. Many thousands of these were provided for marking channels, particularly in conjunction with the minesweeper, to show a swept channel, but were also used by other vessels for locating a mine." (House p.251)

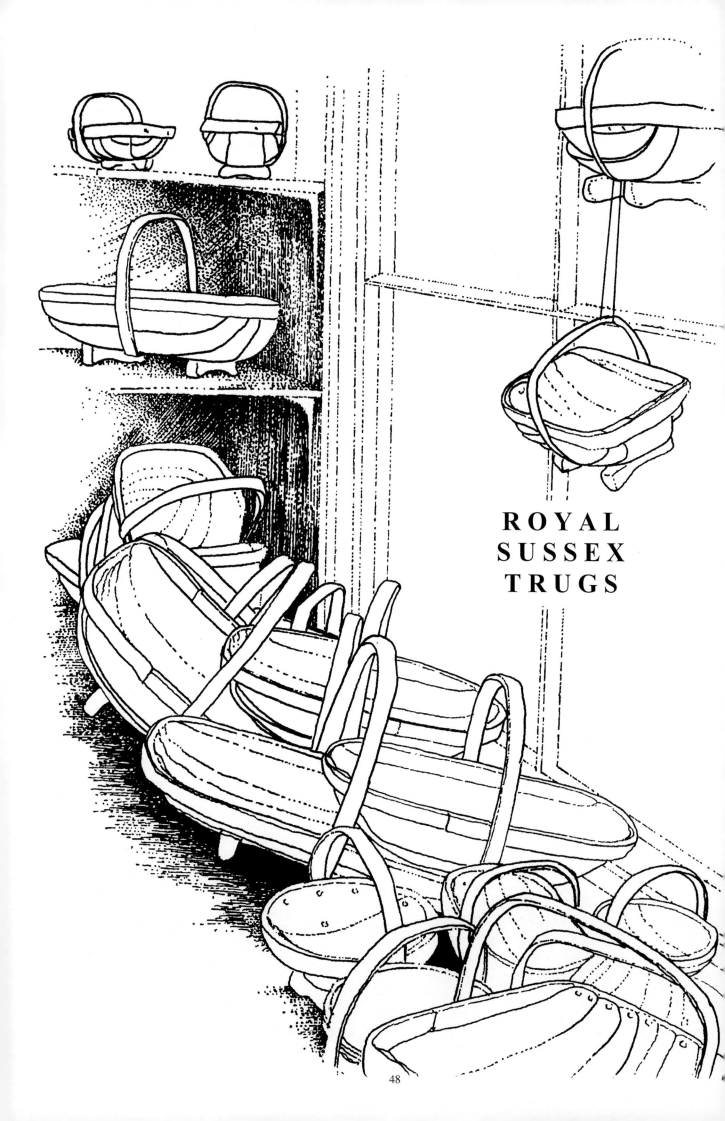

ROYAL
SUSSEX
TRUGS

and then back to London for the International Exhibition of 1885. Today, the business he started is run by Robin Tuppen and about eight craftsmen, who can each make a gross a week. Thus thousands are produced each year, which go all round the world. Other craftsmen around Herstmonceux make them too. They find great favour with gardeners, many of whom become so emotionally attached to their trug that they send them back for restoration rather than buy a new one. Gardeners and their trugs are not easily parted! Production is likely to persist as the craft has attracted young apprentices. Not that they begin in the same way as the most senior craftsman there, who was 81 in 2003, and recalls that when *he* began he had to work the first four months without pay to prove he could stick at it.

Trugs are wooden baskets. They resemble little boats and may derive their name from the Saxon word *troog* for a boat. That's the favoured derivation although the OED gives only the alternative derivation, from Saxon *trog,* meaning a trough. There have been varying designs down through the ages, with the early versions carved out of a solid block of timber, so they could be used for liquids - they survived in use longest for milk in dairies.[1] Today the world centre for their making is an unprepossessing little building of blackened corrugated iron and white weather-boarding. It braves the traffic right beside the busy A271 where it hammers through the village of Herstmonceux. Here they have been making trugs since about 1919, for this was the workshop of the Smiths and it was Thomas Smith who is attributed with redesigning them into today's form and who made trugs famous. That came about in 1851 when he took them to the Great Exhibition and on the first day caught the eye of Queen Victoria. She ordered several as gifts for the Royal family, which he made quickly at Herstmonceux. Then he and his brother trundled them off to London in a handcart. It was a good time. Not only did he get a Gold Medal and a Certificate of Merit (displayed in the Centre) at the exhibition but also the Royal Warrant - hence Royal Sussex Trugs. They became international in 1855 when they won a Silver Medal and a Certificate of Merit in the Paris version of the Great Exhibition - believed to be the first time they were exported. In 1884 they were at the International Forestry Exhibition at Edinburgh

Cleaving a short length with the traditional froe.

Trugs can be made in a wide range of sizes, from little ones, eight inches long, up to big four footers. Big ones held about a bushel, as it was understood in general usage, but in these days of precision measurements that notion is not acceptable for trading. They are constructed with a Chestnut frame and boards of Cricket Bat Willow (see box). The Chestnut is sourced locally from four coppice workers while the Willow comes from Essex as the waste from the cricket bat makers. If the boards were made from Chestnut then they would most likely split. This design accounts for 51% of the production in this workshop[2] in the village. The other 49% are of the newer design using laminated boards, made from Birch plywood but they still have a Chestnut frame. First the Chestnut is riven using a cleaving axe or froe (demonstrated for the sketches by Alan Isted) with the long pieces for big trugs being worked in an A-frame device. The cut surface is smoothed with a drawknife but the bark is retained on the outer surface, and all lengths have this, as the heartwood is not used. Next the lengths have to be bent round into shape and joined into a hoop, without breaking, which is achieved by softening them for ten minutes in a steam chest boiler. They are bent round a former to get the exact shape consistently; it's a wooden block with rounded corners proud of its base block. They hang in their different sizes on the

---

[1] a set of ten were rediscovered in a dairy at Newhaven, Sx.

[2] There are other craftsmen in the district. See, for example, the website for Peter Marden at Herstmonceux.

wall. Each trug will need two hoops: one has the bark inside and will be the handle while the other has the bark on the outside to become the rim. Excess length is trimmed, overlap joints are managed carefully and then nailing finishes the hoop. The rim hoop is slid inside the handle loop at right angles and nailed. Boarding begins with the central basal board, which is called the *centre* and the others, called *seconds* except the last which is the *side*, are then added, overlapping, and nailed in place. Each is some 4-5mm thick and has been prepared with a drawknife on a shaving horse, to make them slightly thinner at the ends. They are then soaked in water to make them pliable. Feet are then added. Thus each piece of a trug is forced gently into a curve and held there, creating a tension, as it tries to spring back straight again. It is this tension that gives a trug its enduring strength - in days before political correctness it was said, "any girl in a garden is improved by having one."

Above - cleaving in the A-frame
Right - using the shaving horse.

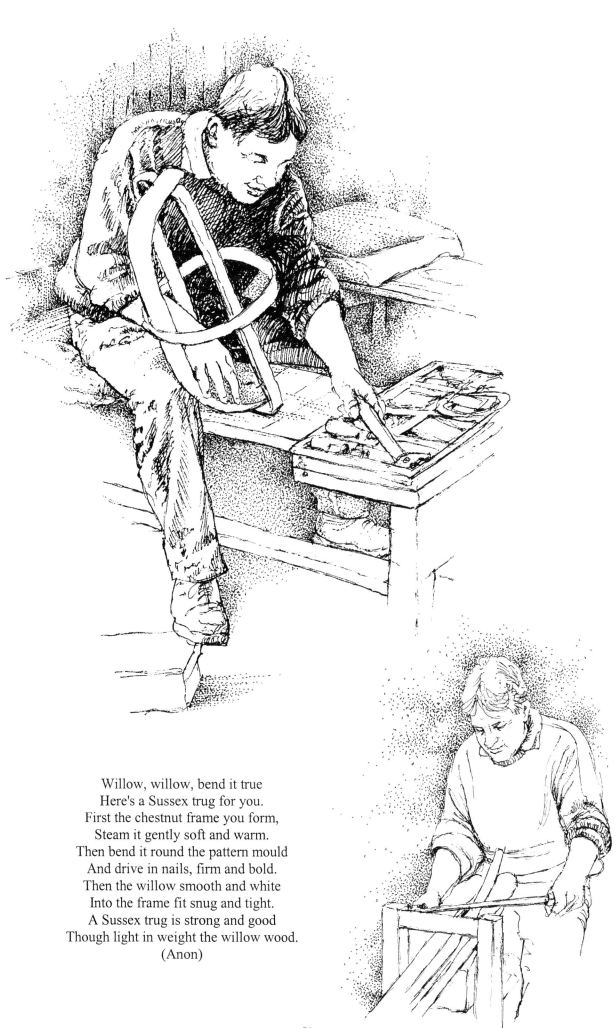

Willow, willow, bend it true
Here's a Sussex trug for you.
First the chestnut frame you form,
Steam it gently soft and warm.
Then bend it round the pattern mould
And drive in nails, firm and bold.
Then the willow smooth and white
Into the frame fit snug and tight.
A Sussex trug is strong and good
Though light in weight the willow wood.
(Anon)

PULPWOOD

Tear a cardboard box and inside is the familiar corrugated layer. If it's British it's made from the timber of broad-leaved trees and comes from the only industrial plant in Britain that makes it: the St Regis Company at Sudbrook, by the Severn Bridge, in South Wales. Technically it is known as 'semi-chemical fluting' or SCF for short. There are only three other places in Britain where timber, known industrially as pulpwood, is converted into wood pulp but they all use Spruce. One specialises in newsprint but is converting to recycled wood; another specialises in magazine paper while the third produces the card used in packaging.

Michael Henderson of St Regis travels the country to buy up timber: he needs some 220,000 tonnes a year. Of that, some 10,000 tonnes will be Chestnut, mostly from the South East, such as the Cowdray Estates at Midhurst, Sussex. The rest is made up from whatever else he can get, as he has to compete with the firewood merchants. Beech burns fast as a fuel, making it less desirable for that purpose, so Michael Henderson is better able to get that. It is his most important tree, totalling about 60% of his material. In second place is Oak but that only amounts to some 15-16% of his needs. The rest is made up from whatever else he can get and the list he reels off is endless - so there is a use for wild Rhododendron after all!

Even with modern technology there are various ways of converting a tree into a cardboard box. The process used at Sudbrook is to chip the wood on arrival and so different trees end up mixed together on the chip pile. They are not deliberately mixed since mixing is not necessary at all. Then the chippings are washed to rid them of grit etc. After that they go into a *digester* where, under conditions of heat and pressure, they are treated with sodium sulphite to plasticise the ligin - that's the woody material in the tree cells and they want as much of that as they can get out of the chips. Next, it is refined and then water is added - lots of water - one part pulp to 99 parts water. This solution is sprayed under pressure on to wire to trap the fibres. It is of course 99% wet and will be dried to 10% at which stage it can be rolled off as paper. There the Sudbrook story ends, as the rolls take to the road, destined for other factories that corrugate it ready for box manufacture.

TIMBER

You would think that a mature Chestnut, with its single great column of trunk, would be enough to thrill any timber merchant. This is not so. Look at any sawn tree stump and a difference between Chestnut and all other forest trees in Britain is apparent immediately. There is not the familiar division between heartwood and sapwood. Indeed there does not appear to be any sapwood at all, because it is restricted to just a few narrow annual rings immediately inside the bark. Anything older starts getting absorbed as heartwood into the main body of the timber. That means there's very little pure sapwood to cut off as waste when it comes into use but it also means a lot of sappy growth is being incorporated into the heartwood. Although this suits some craftsmen (see trugs), others find that the timber develops weaknesses as it dries out. Thus it is particularly important that it should be seasoned slowly and carefully. To the woodworker these weaknesses are known as 'shakes'. They radiate out across the wood from the centre, as star shakes, and arise as concentric cracks where the annual rings begin to separate, creating ring and cup shakes. In Chestnut these often combine to make a mosaic of flaws across the timber, that reduces its strength. Thus there is no substantial history in Britain of chestnut timbers being used for structural purposes or for fine furniture. Instead, the timber cleaves well and so it has been employed for wood of small dimensions that can be taken out between the flaws, such as boards from which to make roofing shingles.

Since there are other fine timber trees from which to choose there has been little incentive to investigate the formation of shakes from either a technical or an arboricultural viewpoint and so they remain little understood today. The general consensus of opinion is that the worst soils produce the worst shakes but of course Chestnut is one of the trees that succeeds on poor soils. Shakes develop in a few decades. Trees fifty to sixty-five years old will have them. On deeper richer soils they can be left safely till they are eighty-five or even older. There is a belief that there is a correlation between the spiralling of the bark outside and the formation of shakes inside, so trees must be cut before the spiralling develops. Even so, they are not going to produce massive sound timbers *consistently* so the growing of Chestnut as a timber crop has always been very limited. Nearly *all* chestnut timber marketed in Britain today has been imported.

Most people seem to love the smell of freshly cut wood and each tree has its own smell but the difference between Oak and Chestnut is barely perceptible. Pick up a block of wood for closer inspection and again there is very little difference. In experienced hands, Chestnut might feel lighter, averaging 30-45 pounds per cubic foot when Oak is about 45 pounds. The crucial point is that there are no medullary rays in Chestnut whereas in Oak their presence gives the beautiful silver-graining, (depending how the timber has been sawn). Nevertheless, Chestnut has the same beautiful rich brown colour and good ring markings, albeit rather porous. Thus it finds a welcome with furniture-makers, especially as it takes finishes well, and shrinks very little as it dries out. That renders it very stable in the fluctuating humidity of offices and homes. Indeed many craftsmen claim it is the most stable wood in British craftsmanship. Like Oak, it is acidic and will corrode ferrous fastenings, creating a black stain, so brass should be used instead. It is accused of having a "slight blunting effect on cutting tools" - well what craftsman never expects to sharpen his tools?

Working our forests has evolved primarily around Oak and conifers, rather than Chestnut.

CHESTNUT IN OUR BUILDINGS

So much of the beauty of Britain lies in the diversity of its architectural heritage. How often does Chestnut contribute to that? The simplest answer is a dismissive *hardly at all*, but let's review it a little more closely.

STRUCTURAL TIMBERS

Starting with the structures themselves, we have next to no information on early scaffolding and yet coppiced Chestnut would provide long, straight poles of notable durability. Medieval records were primarily financial, of the building itself, and were not interested in the species of tree employed during its construction. The most frequent exception was for the great roof beams because those were in short supply and incurred extra charges for locating and transporting them. Famously, Oak (*illus. above*) was the universal tree for providing all great timbers plus the framing timbers. With the development of modern tourism came a demand for guide books and soon all our old churches etc. had one. What they needed was to be able to claim

that their building was just that little bit different from the norm. So there arose a number of claims that the roof was of Chestnut instead of Oak. Examples range up the scale from tiny parish churches to the chapel of King's College, Cambridge, St. Albans Cathedral and even the Great Hall of the Palace of Westminster. The last claim attacked national pride in 'English Oak' and caused quite a degree of disquiet in Victorian England. The matter was settled, eventually, by one of the foremost botanists of the time, Dr. John Lindley. After examining the Westminster roof he duly pronounced it being made of Durmast Oak (*Quercus petraea*). Elsewhere, communities still cling devoutly to their local Chestnut attribution and argue emotionally against any suggestion of it being otherwise. Salzman investigated the claims for his *Building in England down to 1450* and found only one genuine Chestnut roof.[1]

Documentary evidence is just as rare. There is one example, dating from 1278, when Milton (next to Sittingbourne) in Kent supplied Chestnuts for the works at Dover Castle. They supplied 100 'roboro', which Rackham[2] believes would have been the trunks of

---

[1] In some instances Chestnut can be notoriously difficult to distinguish from Oak. If it has been cut in such a way as to reveal medullary rays then it is Oak.

[2] Rackham; *Ancient Woodlands*; p.331

pollards. In other words, these were substantial timbers as opposed to scaffolding poles from a cropped coppice. Rackham suggests these were not simply the trunks but were trunks that had died. They would then have been of no further use for cropping by the tenants or those with commoners' rights, so they would revert to the landlord, to be disposed of at will. On occasions when the landlord was the king, they were given sometimes as donations. Royal gifts were recorded so we know more about them.[3]

Thus as far as we know today, Chestnut was rarely used for constructional timbers, from the time of our earliest buildings through to the present. When landowners took more interest in timber trees, in the 17th century, they were put off Chestnut by John Evelyn who warned: "*I cannot celebrate the tree for its Sincerity, it being found that (contrary to the Oak) it will make a fair shew outwardly, when 'tis all decayed and rotten within; but this is in some Sort recompensed, if it be true, that the Beams made of Chestnut-tree have this Property, that being somewhat brittle, they give Warning and premonith the Danger by a certain Crackling that it makes....*"[4] This notion that the beams crackle a warning before they collapse is not drawn from his experiences in England. He is drawing upon the writing of Pliny, in Roman times, but Pliny was citing the Greek Theophrastus, who knew the tree was used for roof beams.[5] Interestingly, the Chestnut isn't mentioned at all in the timber section of the ten volume treatise on architecture by Vitruvius.[6] In the 4th century CE it gets added to the list of structural timbers by Palladius.[7] It is not until the Popes are rebuilding Rome in the 15-16th centuries CE that Chestnut gets used a lot.[8]

Today it is possible to have an old timber-framed building made of Chestnut because there are companies that buy up old examples in France. They have them dismantled and transported over to Britain for re-erection. Alternatively, there's the option of a brand new building of advanced technology. These are known as 'gridshell' structures. The first great pioneering building of this type was by the German, Frei Otto, at Mannheim in 1975. He had looked at the way coral in the sea could look so light and delicate and yet be so very strong. Since then, there have been other studies and various interpretations and adaptations of the basic idea. Materials range from steel at the British Museum development to Oak at the Weald and Downland Museum. For Chestnut, turn to the Woodland Enterprise Centre at Flimwell, East Sussex. It is not described as a pure gridshell but as having a modular gridshell roof - a vault of beautiful Chestnut lattice-work.

---

[5] French sources, such as Bourdu, are saying there is no evidence that the Greeks used Chestnut in building.

[6] there are two; this one is Marcus Vitruvius Pollio, active 46-30 BCE

[7] see Meiggs pp 240-1

[8] Meiggs p.382

---

[3] Rackham; Ancient Woodlands p.182

[4] *Silva*; Bk 1, Ch. VIII

One of the great beauties of this type of building is that its prime material is a renewable resource. Working existing coppices to their full potential is good for both the rural economy and the conservation of the countryside. Part of its intended purpose at Flimwell was to highlight this very potential. It takes 15 tonnes of Chestnut to make such a building and there is so much woodland in the South East that it puts on an extra 100,000 tonnes of growth per year - so a lot of buildings can be produced without ever touching the basic reserve.

Crucially, these developments use small-size timber, known as 'small round wood' or SRW, which ranges from 2-16 inches in diameter. For some twenty-five years now various reports have been highlighting this resource, with little result in positive action. The Forestry Commission census of 1979-82 revealed a potential annual yield from small roundwood of 741,000-816,000 tonnes. Dannatt, in 1991, said Chestnut accounted for 12-17%, or an estimated annual yield of 92,200-138,300 tonnes. Of that, 70% would come from Kent. Since then the trees have continued to grow and the figures are higher. Wood-fuelled power stations were one option investigated and found to be viable. Sussex and France, with EU funding, are investigating a new composite material based upon Chestnut. On the whole the resource is still waiting to be brought back into economic use. It only takes five hectares of Chestnut to "grow a new building every year." The Chestnut for the Flimwell Woodland Enterprise Centre used very small pieces - only 28x75mm - but they were remoulded at Newcastle into 10m lengths. A lot of modern technology and a lot of co-operative effort from architects and industries brought the building plans to fruition but in the end you still need craftsmen. The website records "certain difficulties ensued" because the woodworkers only had experience of working softwoods, not hardwoods, like Chestnut.[9]

Finally, on the subject of buildings themselves, an odd one cropped up on a visit to the Rural Life Centre for the chapter on hop-poles. Preserved at the Centre is

[9] with thanks to Nigel Braden for assistance with the Flimwell material

Shingled spire, Byfleet, Surrey

a little chapel, including detached campanile, made of Chestnut, to the extent that half-rounds have been faced onto panels in geometric designs. The bark was left on so it must have looked very hoary when it all started to peel off. The little plaque showing to the left of the door is also of Chestnut, inscribed *WOMEN ARE EXPECTED TO WEAR A HAT OR HEAD SCARF IN THIS CHAPEL* followed by *HEAD SCARFS PROVIDED*. Dating from the 19th century, it was one of a group of Non-Conformist Chapels founded in West Surrey and this particular one was at Eashing, where it was squeezed into the steep roadside bank above the bridge. It gets commented upon in early guidebooks. Eventually it was put on wheels and trundled off to be a chicken shed, so it was in a bit of a sad state by the time it got rescued and brought to the Centre. Once it was cleaned up it was found to be in a very bad state of repair and so the Chestnut panels are modern recreations. One original panel was kept and is usually on display nearby. Having seen it, more examples of the diagonal technique were soon being spotted all around West Surrey, for porches and sheds etc. Whenever it was possible to inspect them closely they were all found to be of softwood, usually Scots Pine, rather than Chestnut.

SHINGLES

Turning to roofs, Chestnut makes excellent shingles (wooden tiles). A coppice pole is cleft and cut into the tile lengths and there are still a few craftsmen doing this. Ideally the widest shingles are used for the bottom layers of the roof and the smallest nearest to top but shingles, like tiles, are now getting ordered in standard uniform sizes. In France they are still used widely whereas in England they have always had to compete with Oak and it is the Oak that dominates. In many parts of the country, shingles are never to be seen, but in the South East they are the norm for church spires (illus. above - Byfleet, Surrey). There are many hundreds of them. Technically, they are 'chamfer-edge spires'[10] from the clever design that ensures an octagonal spire converts to a square before it reaches the tower. Oak is still the preferred material although they may have to be made upon demand. Such was the case with the spire restoration at Newdigate, Surrey, where the villagers filmed the whole process, starting with the felling of the Oaks. Cheaper versions are made from Western Red Cedar - used popularly for the roofs of bus-shelters. It isn't known when the craft started but there are references to shingles in the Middle Ages. One of Britain's very first castles, Hen Domen, built for Roger de Montgomery c.1070, is thought to have been shingled because the archaeologists can't find clay tiles.[11]

WALLS AND CEILINGS

Prehistoric man invented the famous wattle-and-daub walling that got adapted into panels for infilling medieval timber framed buildings and for creating internal partition walls. Chestnut could have been used for the wattles where it was available since the practice of weaving Chestnut panels has come down to us through hurdle making. At the end of the Middle Ages people began to replace the wattle infills with fashionable new brick and by the 17th century it was becoming commonplace to hide all the timbering behind brick. It should not show inside either and so wall beams and beams across the ceilings were hidden behind uninterrupted expanses of plaster. The technique to achieve this effect is known as 'lath-and-plaster'. By the 18th century imported softwood was becoming available widely for the framing of cheaper housing so lath-and-plaster became the norm since nobody wanted their softwood framing to show. The structure of the house is still hidden under plaster today.

The basic technique, with some regional variations, is to nail long wooden strips or laths, about an inch wide, across the beams in close succession, leaving about a quarter of an inch between them. The gap forms the 'key' to hold the plaster that is pressed into it. The first coat has animal hair, usually from horses or goats,

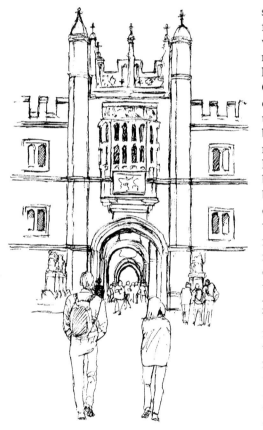

compounded into it as a binder and to stop it crumbling. Chestnut poles can be riven down readily to make the long laths but there are only a few craftsmen left who still have the skill to cleave it. That became a problem for the restoration of Hampton Court Palace (illus.) after the fire of 1986. Some of the lath and plaster walls had been destroyed and although the craftsmen were prepared to produce replacement laths it was realised that so many were needed that there was no way they could be made within the time limit of the contract. Take too long and penalty clauses are invoked. Thus expanded metal laths were used for the ceiling of Cartoon Gallery. Otherwise the only other concession to modernity was to replace the horse hair with sisal and to use a smaller proportion of goat hair.

Finally, before leaving the subject of walls, a brief note on framing holes in them, for windows and doors. Whereas many countries employed hardwood frames, including Chestnut, in Britain softwood dominated the market. It stayed that way until double-glazing brought about a national modernisation and then hardwoods, like Mahogany, were back in fashion. This has declined both through environmental concerns for the destruction of tropical rain forests and also in face of determined opposition from suppliers of various plastic-coated metal alternatives with their promise of never needing painting. Although Chestnut has been reconsidered for the purpose it is too expensive in comparison with Scandinavian impregnated redwood. Some systems of impregnation are to be outlawed, depending upon which chemicals they use (such as arsenic) and so the situation may change.

FLOORING

As with structural timbers, Chestnut has always lost out to Oak for flooring. Early flooring was of a size that readers would think of as 'planks' rather than the floorboards they are familiar with today. Such sizes were not available readily in Britain. The French used them and now there are British companies that reclaim old French floors and import them for re-use in Britain. They can be just as beautiful and hard-wearing as Oak and so are in demand while bare wooden floors are once again fashionable. They are also benefiting from the current rejection of tropical hardwoods that have not been harvested from a renewable source.

The planks have been superseded by 'strips,' for what are known as 'hardwood strip floors'. They can be

[10] The Pevsner guides call them 'broach' spires but that doesn't distinguish them from spires with true broaches.
[11] Morris

made from wood of smaller dimensions, which could come from coppiced stock. British flooring manufacturers work usually with material that is an inch thick and either three or six inches wide. Lengths range from six to ten feet, although there is that peculiar British resistance to metrication that means timber is traded in metric lengths but the British stick to old fashioned imperial measurements for width and thickness. The greater the length the more likely it is to be impaired by knots and shakes, so cropping for this particular outlet is not usually economic, unless there are outlets for the rejects. They can still go for flooring because Chestnut is used for both 'hardwood block floors' and 'hardwood mosaic floors'. Some manufacturers buy this in kiln dried to an 8-10% moisture content while other companies have their own kilns and prepare the material themselves. The end result is a fine floor, either golden brown or a warm grey. They can be susceptible to yellow sap staining which can be left to fade away or disguised under a light coat of coloured finish.

With so much Chestnut under-utilised this is one market that has been explored for development. In particular, the possibility of using it for 'pre-finished composite parquet' has been explored. The notion is to laminate a Chestnut surface layer onto a less attractive cheaper base block. The surface Chestnut or 'lamella' is produced by putting the timbers either through a multi-blade vertical sawing system or by surface slicing. Timbers need to be at least 18cm in circumference and at least 1.3m long, which would suit our overgrown

The Georgians developed the use of softwood into all aspects of our homes and once they had invented white lead paint were able to produce the white weatherboarding that is such a regional style today in the Thames Valley and districts of the South Eastern counties.

coppice wood. Again, knots and shakes are a major problem. They mean that only about 10% of the pole is actually usable - that's only a third of what can be got out of Oak. It doesn't sound very viable but there is optimism that this *could* be developed into an economic process for a product that certainly has a market.

The British seem to have a resistance to being enterprising when it comes to timber. Again and again, during the research for this study, there were tales of woe concerning the breakdown of marketing procedures. The estate manager of Painshill Park found he needed to remove Chestnut as part of the restoration programme and decided to sell it towards the restoration funds. A timber merchant was keen to buy it but failed continually to collect it on the agreed date. After several months the Chestnut was hindering progress and had to be burned. That scenario was reported rather frequently. Another version was reported by Clive Harrison who specialises in flooring but has to import French timber. He noted that a major wildlife conservation body that owns a Chestnut wood in Essex had brought in contractors to fell it - "*I told them the price I paid in France for the chestnut flooring and haulage up to the UK, inviting them to turn the logging into flooring. They were not interested however, finding it easier to sell the wood as firewood or for stakes.....the real shame is that parts of France are heavily wooded: e.g. Dordogne Department land surface is 46% wooded. The working of the woods provides rural employment - small wood mills are plentiful - and there is an economic incentive when giving up arable or sheep grazing to revert the land to woodland.*"

FURNITURE

The Roman mosaics in the Royal Palace at Fishbourne stun thousands of visitors every year but it is more difficult to imagine the rooms complete, decorated and furnished. Imaginings should include tables and those could well have been of warm brown chestnut, perhaps a fine one brought from the Mediterranean and presented as tribute. The Romans esteemed fine furniture and chestnut tables in particular, from trees at Sinope. There are references to these in the contemporary writings, providing we are right in believing that 'nut wood' means Chestnut. The references to the 'mountain nuts' at Sinope are almost certainly Chestnut whereas other references to 'nut wood' probably referred to Walnut. It's frustrating that the writers had no consistent use of plant names until the familiar Latin names into general use at the end of the Republic.[12] Thus the Romans were able to bring to Britain an appreciation of fine furniture that was of long standing in the Mediterranean and Near Eastern cultures. The beautiful throne and beds of Pharaoh Tutankamen are a remarkable survival from the Ancient World that leave us marvelling at the craftsmanship. This was due in part to so much of the region being bereft of good timber trees. Carpenters had to pay dearly for imported wood; hence the fame of the Cedars of Lebanon, and they lavished consummate skill upon it.

---

[12] see Meiggs p.421

The best Roman architecture in Britain was designed to be weatherproof but for hundreds of years afterwards homes were liable to be cold and damp in winter, which put furnishings at risk of rot. It wasn't till the reign of Henry VIII that there was a marked improvement, reflected in the development of English furniture. By then timber from British Chestnut trees was available but scarce: "*Deal and chestnut were comparatively rare woods and correspondingly prized.*"[13] Oak was more durable and became pre-eminent. Chestnut was used as a substitute, especially for panelling, despite it not having the silver-grain of the Oak, but was used much more rarely for furniture. That became a persistent tradition, although John Evelyn recorded it as being rated second after Oak and *"one of the most sought after by the Carpenter and Joyner."* He lists tables, chests, chairs, stools and bedsteads.[14]

It remained an Oak substitute and always inferior to Oak but both were soon eclipsed by Walnut and then with the expansion of world trade by exotic timbers like Teak and Mahogany. Usage of Chestnut persisted as cottage furniture and got a boost with the cottage orné style of the late 18th and early 19th centuries. In the later 19th century the nostalgic looking-back to a supposed Golden Age of the countryside brought a lot of 'rustic' furniture back to prominence. Windsor chairs, named after their prime market place, but made around High Wycombe, Buckinghamshire, took "*considerable quantities*" for turned chair legs.[15] For joint stools and chair rails it is an ideal choice because it is so stable in the fluctuating humidity of a home that the joints do not loosen. With the expanding middle classes and the development of leafy suburbs in Edwardian times there was a demand again for an affordable, lighter, Oak substitute and so Chestnut was "*almost entirely used in the manufacture of so called oak stationery cabinets, and all furniture of that class…*"[16] Then fashion changed to tropical timbers before a reversal to sustainable European woods and so by 1980 Lewington was able to record its use by the British furniture manufacturers albeit with imported Chestnut That is still largely the case today, despite many derelict coppices having reached suitable dimensions for a range of furniture demands. Nevertheless, there are individual craftsmen scattered throughout Britain who turn home-grown wood into very beautiful bespoke furnishings. Whole kitchen and bedroom suites are available too.

Now that gardens are viewed as 'outdoor rooms' it has been boom time for outdoor furniture. Although the Victorians incorporated rustic seats into their garden designs it was not until the last few decades of the 20th century that the British took to this with enthusiasm. Not only has global warming given us a greater likelihood of better summers through which to sit out in the garden but there has been more opportunity, occasioned by shorter working hours, longer holidays and early retirement. Cheaper Continental holidays have introduced many people to the pleasures of dining and relaxing out of doors, which they have copied back home. These factors, not common to everyone, have been backed by a new enthusiasm for gardening in general. More people want to be out in their gardens, and design them increasingly with seating and eating areas - the Spanish word *patio* has become a familiar addition to the English language.

Certainly there is a surprising number of small-scale manufacturers with Internet websites, offering not just chestnut benches and tables but also pergolas, rose arches, bridges, bird tables etc. Parallel with this has been an increased enthusiasm to sit out in a pub garden with the children, which is again indebted to experiences abroad, and certainly promoted by the pubs. They want robust furniture, resistant to rain and sun, so is often of chestnut - mature coppice poles have been exported, from counties like Sussex, to Spain and there converted into pub garden furniture ready for exporting back to Britain.

Not all outdoor furniture needs to be 'rustic' in the 'rough and ready' sense. In 2002 a new range was launched for the upper end of the market, by Duchy Originals, headed by Prince Charles, to market produce from his Duchy of Cornwall. Chestnut tables and chairs are being made from trees in Aconbury Wood, which is part of the Duchy near Hereford. Only 500 pieces a year will be produced, all numbered and signed with the hallmark of Duchy Originals, Stephen Florence the designer and of the craftsman who made that particular piece. They are worked with traditional skills yet their design is modern and geometric.

Rustic chair made of Chestnut except the seat, which is of Elm. Seats were usually made of Elm since it is so resistant to splitting, not only when in use but when being drilled to take the legs and spindles. (private collection)

[13] Fastnedge p.19
[14] Chapter VII, pp.45-6
[15] Edlin, *Woodland Crafts*; p.48
[16] Braid p.219

NUTS FOR NOURISHMENT
(Beware of nut allergies)

One of the great delights of an autumn walk among Chestnuts is to roll a spiny husk underfoot till it splits open and spills out its nuts. Ignore the two concave empty fruits and retrieve the plump one. Sometimes it's still creamy white with reddening streaks running down from its point. These peel the more easily so bite off the point, rip off the shell, and then fiddle around removing the inner skin. Try biting them in half to expose an edge to start tearing from but use only your teeth, else your mouth will taste the bitterness of the skin. British wild nuts are wrinkled like brains so it can be tricky getting the skin off. Persevere! They are delicious. Book after book will tell you never to eat chestnuts raw and yet they never give a reason. Country children ate handfuls without ruining their day. Warnings about flatulence were well founded but children have never been overly concerned about flatulence.

Caches of chestnuts found by archaeologists at Roman sites[1] remind us how useful were nuts, whether chestnuts or walnuts, for shipping around the Empire. They kept far longer and with less concerns than other fresh foods, if stored properly. They were a ready snack that could be carried and eaten raw by soldiers on manoeuvres, especially the chestnut, which is so much easier to get out of its shell than the walnut. Even when dried and shrivelled, chestnuts were ground into flour (*polenda*) and used in a variety of ways. Today's Continental cookery books still testify to their versatility. They can be used raw, boiled, roasted, steamed or as a purée. Serve in soup or pâté and then as vegetables or as stuffing; the flour makes delicious bread and pastry. Sweet recipes range from chestnut cream to jam and of course the famous *marrons glacés*. A good Continental cookery book will leave you in no doubt how finely you can dine off chestnuts. It has a long tradition since in some areas chestnuts were a staple for 4-6 months of the year. In England,

---

[1] e.g. Caerwent

however, we tend to ignore our native harvest and import from Spain but even then, their seasonal arrival is for a small minority market. That could expand as more households turn increasingly to organic foods.

Chestnuts are very nutritive. Their composition is distinct from other nuts. The fat content is far lower but is of a high quality. It includes important fatty acids such as linoleic, which is important in preventing heart disease. In place of fats there is a higher carbohydrate content, with about 26% starch, so chestnut flour can be substituted for cereal flour for those intolerant of cereals. Then there is about 9% sugars, mainly sucrose but with small amounts of fructose, glucose and maltose. That is why chestnuts are so adaptable between savoury and sweet uses. They have as much protein as milk and again it is of a high quality (comparable to eggs), containing a good balance of essential amino acids, such as cystine, lysine, metheonine and tryptophan. Chestnuts are rich in minerals too, especially potassium, to aid our cell functions, especially those of the nervous system. Other minerals, in descending order of amount are phosphorus, sulphur, magnesium, calcium, chloride, sodium, iron, manganese and copper and zinc. Lastly, the vitamins, topped by vitamin C but this can be destroyed in the cooking. The vitamin B group is not affected by cooking and chestnuts have small amounts of B1 (thiamine) and much more of B2 (riboflavin) plus nicotinic acid (vitamin PP). Actual amounts have not been given since every table looked at differed, sometimes considerably, so read widely if this topic is of importance to you. Beware of mixing British and American data since there are differences in understanding; for example 'niacin' in the United States is applied specifically to nicotinic acid whereas elsewhere 'niacin' is sometimes used to include nicotinamide as well. Most important of all - remember some people are allergic to nuts, including chestnuts.

There is no evidence from Britain that Chestnuts have been planted deliberately as a fruit crop. Henry II granted the right of tithe of chestnuts to the monks of Flaxley Abbey in the Forest of Dean but that documented reference is unique. We are left to conclude that in good mast years the nuts were gathered by those who had the right, for their own consumption, leaving the rest as pig food. There is no indication that they were valued particularly, e.g. court cases over the right to take them. This is surprising when our neighbours in France held them in esteem and devoted hundreds of square miles to them. After the Restoration, when there was both a fresh interest in Chestnut trees and in French culture, it was too late for the Chestnut. They were by then understood to be food for peasants and pigs, as reflected upon by John Evelyn,

"But we give that Fruit to our Swine in England, which is amongst the Delicacies of Princes in other Countries; and being of the larger Nut, is a lusty and masculine Food for Rustics at all Times; and of better

Nourishment for Husbandmen than Coal and Rusty Bacon; yea, or Beans to Boot, instead of which, they boil them in Italy with their Bacon; and in Virgil's Time, they eat them with Milk and Cheese. The best Tables in France and Italy make them a Service....."[2]

There is not enough evidence to reveal the status of chestnuts during the Middle Ages and Tudor times in England. In general, it is said that chestnuts *were* used but we could not find the evidence to support this. Very few 'cookery books' have survived from the period, in the whole of N. W. Europe, let alone Britain. Such as we have, originated in high status households, such as the English royal court of Richard II and therefore do not reflect the country as a whole. There is also the likelihood that such collections contain Continental material that would have been ignored or adapted in Britain. Similarly, an entry of chestnuts in the account books of the great estates, when they sold off surplus produce, does not tell us whether the nuts were for human or animal consumption.

After Evelyn's time, chestnuts creep into the cook books. This is due partly to influences from America, e.g. chestnut stuffing with turkey. Oddly, the printed records of the ethnobotany of the Native Americans are amazingly limited when it comes to the use of the American species of Sweet Chestnut - only the Cherokee, Iroquois and Mohegan were recorded using it[3] - all with Eastern territories in contact with the colonists. To stuff a turkey, *The Art of Cookery Made Plain and Easy* by Mrs Glasse (1747) tells us to roast and skin 1½ lb of chestnuts, salt and pepper them, compound in 8oz of butter and stuff the turkey. For the sauce she says to take the same amount of chestnuts, also roasted and peeled, and simmer in half a pint of good stock. Then thicken with a knob of butter rolled in flour, without leaving lumps, adding diced fried gammon and slices of sausage.[4] Running into many editions through the 18th century was *The Compleat Housewife: or, Accomplish'd Gentlewoman's Companion* by E. S. Smith. It was written for large households, judging by the quantities required - the chestnut pudding needs two quarts of cream and 18 eggs! Not all the quantities are listed as the cook was expected to use her experience and judgement. There is the tempting option of adding lumps of marrow instead of butter prior to baking.[5]

An interesting question in general is to what extent they might have been eaten raw. Basically, as far as we can understand today, there was an avoidance of eating fresh (uncooked) fruit and vegetables. This arose out of the theory of the four humours - that all of creation was a balance between the four elements and that these gave rise to the temperaments of people. Thus air (deemed warm and moist) gave rise to the sanguine; fire (warm and dry) gave rise to the choleric; water (cold and moist) gave rise to the phlegmatic while earth (cold and dry) gave rise to the melancholic. Thus fruit and vegetables were seen to be the product of earth, water and air and in need of being tempered with fire - cooked. This is quite possibly why there was this tradition that cold moist phlegmatic chestnuts should not be eaten raw. It gives rise to the image of villagers in past eras cooking all their food in one pot over the fire. Whatever their principles of what constituted a good meal, fuel shortages from time to time, would deny them regular cooked meals. The regularity of famine years would have forced chestnuts into their diets. No wonder Evelyn said they were the food of rustics. What we do know is that hazelnuts (cobnuts) *were* eaten raw by Shakespeare's time; the archaeologists knew when they'd discovered the foundations of the Globe Theatre because they started unearthing quantities of nut shells from where audiences had taken them to the performance to eat like modern popcorn.

TO ROAST CHESTNUTS

Roast them in their brown outer husks but they must be pricked before roasting to give them an air hole otherwise they will explode! Include just one that has *not* been pricked and when that explodes you know they are cooked. If using a microwave oven be sure to cover the nuts to avoid damage from the explosion!

TO FREEZE CHESTNUTS

Boil to soften and remove skin - blanch - open freeze - put in storage container.

TO SKIN CHESTNUTS

Before cooking, chestnuts need the outer brown shell removing and then the inner skin, which tastes bitter.

Boil gently in water (some people add a pinch of salt for savoury dishes) until soft, which takes about 20 mins. Peel skin off. This is easier if the nut has been scored round with a sharp knife before boiling.

[2] Evelyn; Silva; p.57.
[3] Moerman p.142
[4] recipe provided by Peter Cockerill.
[5] text provided by Dr. Beverley Weston

AVENUES, PARKS AND VETERANS

Thin wintry sunshine filtering across Cowdray House made this a beautiful ruin to draw, although the diffusion of shadow and detail made it difficult. The great house was destroyed by fire in 1793 and was never rebuilt as the fire was seen as fulfilment of a curse. Today it still stands roofless at the end of a great causeway across water meadows, just at the end of the main street of Midhurst in West Sussex, in the heart of the local Chestnut country. It was inherited in 1492 by Sir David Owen who was the son of none other than the great Owain Glyndwr, national hero of the Welsh. He started the house that stands today and lived there till his death in 1535, even though he sold it in 1529 to Sir William Fitzwilliam. The new owner continued to develop the house, being granted his license to crenellate in 1533. This was a man whose political position demanded that he made a fine statement. He was made Earl of Southampton in 1537 and Lord Keeper of the Privy Seal in 1539. He died in 1542 and the house passed to his half-brother, Sir Anthony Browne, another great Court favourite (made Lord High Admiral in 1537, Master of the Horse in 1539). He was among the many beneficiaries at the Dissolution of the Monasteries; he got Bayham Abbey, already featured in this book, and Easebourne Priory right here next to the house.[1] Thus within sixty years Cowdray became one of the foremost houses in the country, hosting Elizabeth I in 1591.

Part of Sir William Fitzwilliam's statement was the construction of the central gatehouse (illus. right), which is of goldy sandstone with paler quoins. The quoins are not built in regularly so perhaps they were hidden originally under plaster and limewash. What a brilliant white statement that would have made in the landscape, although not one that would find favour with everybody today. Alongside this building programme would have been the maintenance and development of an equally impressive park. Visitors in general, as far as we can tell, would have noted with satisfaction a pastoral landscape of rolling grassland, furnished with fine specimen trees, well stocked with deer, sheep and some cattle. Into this landscape

saplings would have been added on a regular basis as their elders were felled for timber, providing for example, the great roof beams for the new house. It looks as though Cowdray, like other English estates at the time, was including the planting of Chestnuts. It may have been a new fashion since there are so few survivors in Britain from earlier periods. Perhaps it was a French idea brought to this country with the artists and craftsmen employed by Henry VII when he opened up the country to foreign ideas. One survivor at Cowdray is believed to be the second oldest in the country, after the Tortworth Chestnut, and there is another which also has a girth of over thirty feet.

---

[1] history from Pevsner p.195

The granary on its staddle stones has been moved to the grass on the domestic side of the ruins. It's a reminder that the great estates were largely self-sufficient. Just four estates once covered nearly the whole of West Sussex and even today those of Cowdray still cover some 16,500 acres. Despite losing its great house it has continued as a productive unit of the rural economy. Woodland makes up about 35%, of which about 14% (or 900-1,000 acres) are of Chestnut coppice, still being worked.[2] Going back to the later 19th century, Cowdray never turned to Hop pole production but concentrated more on staves for the coopers making fish barrels. That was superseded in the 20th century by the production of poles for chestnut paling fencing, which it still produces. Increasingly, nowadays, it grows poles for cleft fencing, since the traditional Oak is becoming difficult to get in the right sizes.[3] Thus Cowdray is still a working estate, as it has been for hundreds of years. In its landscape there are a few tantalising old Chestnuts to remind us of its glory days in Tudor times, when Chestnuts came to the fore. They were still favoured two hundred years later when Capability Brown was redesigning English parks, including this one. These ideas are explored now in more detail.

AVENUES

Chestnuts in good autumn colour can outshine the Oaks in the parks. They have been used for their ornamental value since at least the mid 16th century, and that included lining them up as avenues, but the early history of avenues is very poorly documented. Despite all the books on garden history and design there is scant material available on their development in Britain. The first popular gardening book in English was *The Gardener's Labyrinth* by Thomas Hill, published in 1577, and in chapter XII he treats *Of the Framing of Herbs, Walles, and Alles in a Garden*. It is written as though the concept of tree-lined walks would be familiar to his reader already. Continental Renaissance garden design was in advance of ours and a few hours in a library of books on the history of British gardening soon reveals that writers believe avenues were introduced from the Continent. Probably that is so but when those same writers do not cite the earliest examples or even earliest documentation it leaves room for further enquiry. Even if Continental Renaissance developments are taken as the starting point, who promoted the idea? It needs somebody inspired by Continental experiences, who can himself inspire others, to foresee that a row of bare 'twigs' newly planted will, one day, be a grand landscape feature. That person looks like being John Evelyn, who wrote of Chestnuts that,

"For Avenues to our Country Houses, they are a Magnificent and Royal Ornament"......

He addressed the Royal Society on the subject of trees in 1662 and it was expanded for publication by 1664,[4] as *Silva*. This was the first major work on trees in Britain. It must have required many hours of devotion, since it is large and detailed and was of course laboriously written out by hand with a dip pen, often in poor light. The book had the extended title: *a Discourse of Forest Trees and the Propagation of Timber in His Majesty's Dominions*. In other words, this project was thoroughly Royalist - written by a Royalist and delivered to the Royal Society, for the future well being of the king's realm. That realm had only just been reinstated after eleven years as a republican Commonwealth. It was only in 1660 that

---

[2] including the Phoenix Walking Stick Company, the St Regis Paper Company and J. E. Homewood featured in this book

[3] info. courtesy of the head forester, Donald Macdonald

---

[4] *Silva,* Book I, Ch. VIII

the heir to the throne returned from exile to take up his kingship as Charles II.

Charles had spent nine years exiled in the French Court - the Court of King, Louis XIV, the Sun King, who spent lavishly upon gardens and landscapes. This was a king who really knew how to impose royal supremacy upon a landscape and now Charles needed to assert the same on his own realm. He determined that it should be achieved in part by the use of landscape and so he turned to the man who had done it for Louis.

That chief officer was André le Nôtre - third generation of a family of master royal gardeners. He was more than a gardener. He had trained in architecture and painting too and therefore drew all the visual arts into royal service. He developed the designs of Renaissance gardens on a grand scale that would assert royal supremacy like nothing before them. He also had the temperament to design and to supervise his plans right down to the last little details. In particular, he was working on Vaux le Vicomte (1655-61) at the very time Charles was there in the royal court. Charles returned to England just before work started on Versailles (1661-1715). Nevertheless Charles knew that this was what he wanted.

Felbridge

There wasn't so much room in England to be as expansive as in France but the king's thoughts turned to his country retreat at Greenwich. Here the park was big enough and is believed to be one of the schemes for which Charles consulted Le Nôtre. It is thought also that John Evelyn was consulted. It would be almost unbelievable if he had not been, especially as he lived nearby at Deptford where he had created a grand garden in the French style at Sayers Court.[5] Thus the Greenwich deer park came in for drastic modification. Maybe there was some suggestion of design and avenues already. The cutting of long sight lines, or rides, through the trees was part of the stratagem of stag hunting. These were going to be redesigned into the great vistas of the French style, including of course, new avenues. We know Chestnuts

were included since some have survived until today.[6] Indeed, they are thought to be the oldest surviving *planted* trees in English garden/landscape design.[7]

Greenwich was influential by example but it was the king's London scheme that trained people in the ideas. These then spread to the estates of the nobility. The king needed to have a park much nearer the heart of London, preferably adjoining St. James's Palace, to accommodate outdoor Court life as per Versailles. Thus St. James's Park was redesigned but there wasn't much room to be expansive in Westminster; it would never rival Versailles. Nevertheless it fulfilled its political and social purpose. Its lasting value rests in the later works of designers who were associated with it.

Firstly the king drew directly upon French experience for creating this park, by employing three members of the Mollet family, principally André. It was he who had made the style accessible to a wider public by publishing his *Le Jardin de Plaisir* in 1651, while employed by Queen Christina of Sweden. He thus had experience of working with royal courts. It's thought that it was he who worked out the new designs with Charles, possibly in consultation with le Nôtre, but apparently the plans have not survived. To ensure proper maintenance of the park Mollet trained the English - in particular the new Keeper, John Rose (1622-1677) who travelled to France and learned from Le Nôtre directly. Rose employed George London[8] whom he also took to France. They became partners and employed Stephen Switzer and Charles Bridgeman. After London's death in 1713 Wise took Bridgeman as his partner (in 1726) and it was Bridgman who later worked with William Kent and Lancelot 'Capability' Brown. Thus there is an amazing chain of influence right through England's notable garden designers until the latter part of the 18th century. The chain starts with formal French Renaissance designs and evolves ultimately into our famous English 'natural' landscape garden.[9] Probably the best-known exponent of that is Lancelot

---

[5] nothing has survived of this; the present park is modern, on the site of the old.

[6] there are plans to restore parts, in the future.

[7] for Scotland see Strathpeffer

[8] and also Henry Wise (1653-1738) who is significant in this chain of landscape designers

[9] see Studley Royal following

'Capability' Brown, who worked on over 140 estates, and favoured Chestnut along with English Elm, Beech, Oak, Lime and Scots Pine. We can still see some of the Chestnuts that he is thought to have planted, as for example at Petworth Park,[10] West Sussex, where he worked in the late 1750s. Some Chestnuts there are thought to pre-date Brown's work and therefore reflect the esteem with which they were held already. In East Sussex, Sheffield Park[11] has connections with Brown's successor, Humphry Repton. Here, the Chestnuts survive in avenue formation, mostly pollarded, and therefore resistant to the great storms of 1987 and the early 1990s that destroyed so much of the tree heritage in the south east. A further Repton association with Chestnuts can be seen on the other side of the country at Ashton Court, Bristol.[12] Here he incorporated pre-existing Chestnut pollards into his designs, along with other ancient trees, of which there are some 500 in all. These, plus the Repton landscape, are of prime national importance, actively conserved as such, and attracting 1.5 million visitors a year.

To display French designs you needed vast acres and that was beyond the means of many wishing to be fashionable. Some of the Royalists had kept their estates through the Civil Wars or had them returned to them at the Restoration, but there were Republicans who had far lesser estates. Inspiration came from the Dutch, who had also experienced a problem over space in their small well-developed country. They had taken the French ideas but developed them as smaller, more intricate, garden schemes with parterres, topiary, etc. They too had avenues but not often room for great forest trees like the Chestnut. Instead, they turned to more manageable trees like the Hornbeam and the Lime[13], which could be cut and pleached etc. They did get some opportunities for avenues of forest trees and to accommodate these they simply reduced the French schemes with parallel files of trees down to a single file on each side. Thus, it is being claimed, French influence came through the Royalists, often with Catholic sympathies, while the Dutch influence, with its Protestant connections, can often be seen in the parks of Puritans.[14] The latter got a boost with the accession of the Dutch Protestant William of Orange, as William III, King of England, in 1689.

Felbridge

Single file avenues won lasting favour in Britain, although it was not exclusive; when George London laid out the avenues in Bushy Park[15] he did use the French multiple files. An interesting example at Croft Castle, Herefordshire, carries the story that the trees were planted (perhaps in 1750) as a map of the ships at the Spanish Armada. Another story has the trees being planted from chestnuts that came off the Spanish ships at the Armada but this is most unlikely; the same story is told variously around Britain for several different plants. These trees are, nevertheless, venerable ancients, some 30 feet in girth[16] filing across the park for half a mile. Sadly, we've heard that they have contracted Ink Spot Disease and are dying, although the National Trust plans to leave them as wildlife habitat rather than remove them.

STUDLEY ROYAL

In terms of the chain of development from the formal Renaissance designs to the English picturesque there is no better site to visit than Studley Royal, four miles west of Ripon, in North Yorkshire. It has been a World Heritage Site since 1987 and attracts 300,000 people a year, making it the National Trust's most popular 'pay' site. It has so much to offer in different fields of interest, including the greatest water gardens in England and the largest of our monastic ruins, the beautiful Fountains Abbey, founded in 1132. Thus there are over 870 years of history to explore.

---

[10] National Trust property; info thanks to head gardener, Gary Liddle

[11] National Trust property; info thanks to head gardener, Andrew Jesson

[12] Bristol City Council

[13] Limes thought to have been introduced by John Tradescant the Elder from one of his plant collecting expeditions to the Continent in 1610/11.

---

[14] remember, this is a bold generalisation with many exceptions

[15] the famous 'chestnut' avenues still in the Park today are of *Horse* Chestnut, not Sweet Chestnut.

[16] which suggests they are older than 1720

*Felbridge; one side of the avenue,
with the highway beyond the trees*

The medieval deer park survives, with specimen Chestnuts, and is still stocked with 500 deer: native Red and the introduced Fallow and Sika. The redesigning of the landscape begins with John Aislabie who inherited the estates in 1693. He became the Member of Parliament for Ripon in 1695 and rose to be Chancellor of the Exchequer in 1718. He was thus a crucial figure when the South Sea Company (founded in 1711) offered to take over a large part of the national debt in 1720. Indeed Aislabee was a principal sponsor and promoted the Bill through Parliament personally. Its success was followed by an enormous increase in value in its shares, only to suffer a catastrophic slump[17] that ruined many investors and brought charges of corruption. Aislabie was expelled from Parliament and barred from holding another public office for life. He retreated to Studley Royal and from 1721 till his death in 1742 he devoted himself to redesigning his park.

He was inspired by Le Nôtre designs - you can still walk the double avenue, with Lime trees on the inside and Chestnut on the outside, leading away from the church and guiding the eye off to Ripon Cathedral far in the distance. He did consult Colen Campbell, who was an exponent of the Palladian style and had published the first volume of his Vitruvius Britannicus in 1715. His Wanstead House (now demolished) became the model of the Palladian country house in England. Colen obviously gave lasting inspiration to Aislabie but the work at Studley Royal was a local effort. The gardener, William Fisher, was selected from the estate workers; the director of operations was another local man, John Simpson, employing local labourers. Not until 1728 was Simpson succeeded by an outsider, Robert Doe, master mason from London. The key element in the design was the transformation of a narrow river valley into a great water garden - not a flourish of fountains but mirrors of still waters reflecting the treescape either side. Aislabie died in 1742 but his son, William, continued the work. He bought the massive ruins of Fountains Abbey in 1767 and was thus able to include them into the developing designs, to be viewed majestically from the Water Garden. Other landowners built their own ruins as fashionable follies but William had the genuine article and the finest in the country at that. Thus the designs run from the Renaissance formal geometric, with grand vistas, at one end of the lake, to the English naturalistic, with the Abbey ruins, at the other end, where it merges into the deer park. This is unrivalled.

The Little Owl has colonised holes in the mature Chestnuts beside the Devil's Punch Bowl, Surrey.

---

[17] 1720; the South Sea Bubble of history books

FELBRIDGE AND ALBURY

Felbridge is just inside Surrey, being on the border with West Sussex, on the outskirts of East Grinstead. Turn off the A264 into Crawley Down Road and look for the village sign in the grass on the right - it depicts one of the Chestnut trees that line both sides of this road just ahead. Leafless winter reveals their dark brown stately boles at their best (illus). Come summer and they nearly disappear into volumes of leafiness, as per the illustration opposite. It's quite easy to miss them altogether! The landscape is much changed but originally the highway was the private carriageway to a country house, now demolished, so that only the Chestnuts survive. Who planted them? Avenues are nigh on impossible to date precisely, without documentary evidence. Local traditions invariably look back to some date of presumed significance and attribute the avenue accordingly. This ends up as 'fact' in the guide books. Thus the Felbridge avenue was remarked upon in 1938 in the Surrey volume of Arthur Mee's King's England series:-

"It has a fine line of 37 chestnuts planted by John Evelyn to mark the coming back of Charles the Second."

Now that *would* be interesting in this context but is it true? Many an early avenue has been attributed to Evelyn for no better reason than his promotion of the idea. In this case, however, the avenue is on land that was formerly part of the estates held by the Evelyn family, from 1588 to 1856, so maybe the claim is well founded. The Felbridge and District History Group have investigated this, in detail.[18] The earliest document to record the avenue is the Board map of 1748, which shows the trees either side of the estate carriageway, except that the northern side is only half its modern length. That had been extended by the time of Roque's map of 1768. Fortunately, for ascertaining a more precise date, there was the possibility of a tree-ring count, since one had been felled pre 1943 and still lay in a garden. A second had been felled in 1993 and was still available for three sections to be cut and counted. In every case there were indecipherable patches but they all pointed to a mid 18th century date. Researchers also tried formulae for estimating age by girth but the trees had a considerable range, from 3.5m-6.2m. Ultimately it was concluded, from all the available evidence, that the avenue was most probably started by Edward Evelyn, who held the estates from 1719-1748.

The researchers calculated the original planting distances, from tree centre to tree centre[19] and thereby ascertained how many trees there were in the present-day gaps. From this it seems that in its prime there were 104 Chestnuts: fifty-two each side. Today just 47 survive and they are not in good condition, possibly due to the hard-surfaced highway and its traffic, and so

Nuthatches will nest in holes in mature trees. They cement a threshold of clay around the hole.

they have been partly pollarded again, to try and re-invigorate them. Calculating the planting distances has been done elsewhere to see whether a pattern emerges by which the age of an avenue could be calculated. So far this hasn't proved very helpful.[20] For one thing, there is a problem over the original measurements, if taken from a French source, since a French foot was not the same length as an English foot, leaving researchers wondering whether this was known and taken into account by the planters.

So Felbridge does not have a John Evelyn avenue but maybe Albury Park does. This Surrey estate was so admired by him that he tried to buy it. Instead, it was bought by Henry Howard, 6th Duke of Norfolk, who developed the park in the current fashion. Evelyn visited several times and no doubt commented favourably upon the garden works because in 1667 he was put in charge of them. Remarkably they remain almost unaltered today and beyond them, in the parkland, are broken rows of ancient Chestnut trees. Enough survive to reveal clearly the layout of former avenues, although today many are enveloped in a confusion of woodland. It is usually presumed that they were planted according to Evelyn's grand design, but there is no surviving early documentation relating to their presence until 1701. At least they survived the devastating gales of 1703 that are said to have killed 8,000 people.[21]

---

[18] see Felbridge in Bibliog. My thanks to the Felbridge Womens' Institute for their assistance.

[19] it was half a chain/33 feet

[20] thanks to Sarah Couch, historic landscape consultant for a discussion on this and the rest of the chapter.

[21] The park is not often open to the public but the end trees of one avenue are passed en route to the old church that does have public access.

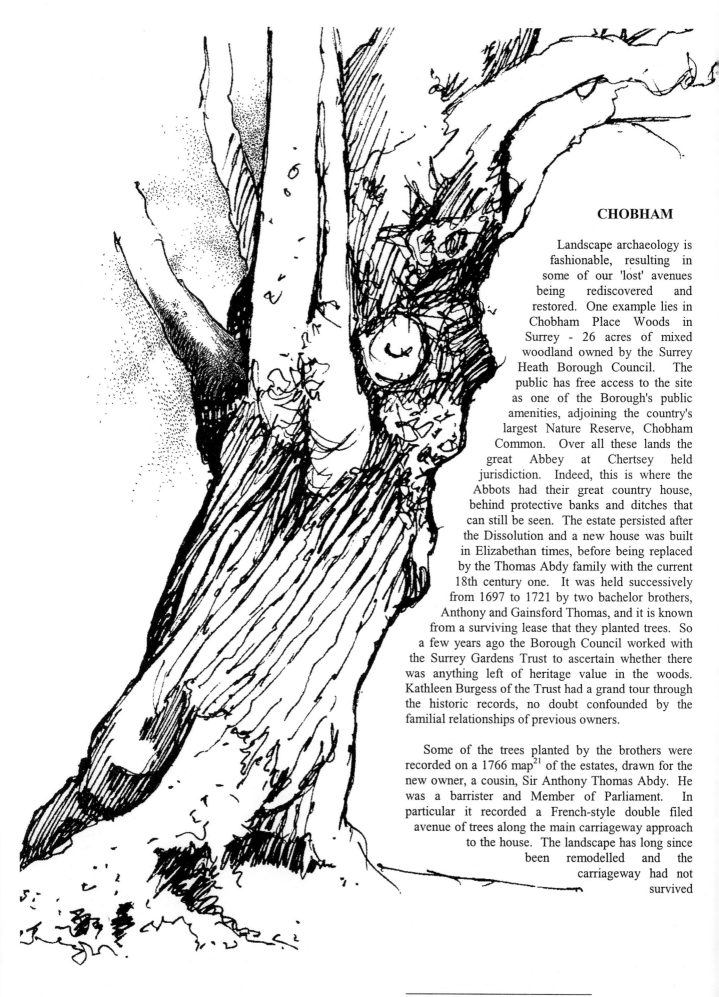

CHOBHAM

Landscape archaeology is fashionable, resulting in some of our 'lost' avenues being rediscovered and restored. One example lies in Chobham Place Woods in Surrey - 26 acres of mixed woodland owned by the Surrey Heath Borough Council. The public has free access to the site as one of the Borough's public amenities, adjoining the country's largest Nature Reserve, Chobham Common. Over all these lands the great Abbey at Chertsey held jurisdiction. Indeed, this is where the Abbots had their great country house, behind protective banks and ditches that can still be seen. The estate persisted after the Dissolution and a new house was built in Elizabethan times, before being replaced by the Thomas Abdy family with the current 18th century one. It was held successively from 1697 to 1721 by two bachelor brothers, Anthony and Gainsford Thomas, and it is known from a surviving lease that they planted trees. So a few years ago the Borough Council worked with the Surrey Gardens Trust to ascertain whether there was anything left of heritage value in the woods. Kathleen Burgess of the Trust had a grand tour through the historic records, no doubt confounded by the familial relationships of previous owners.

Some of the trees planted by the brothers were recorded on a 1766 map[21] of the estates, drawn for the new owner, a cousin, Sir Anthony Thomas Abdy. He was a barrister and Member of Parliament. In particular it recorded a French-style double filed avenue of trees along the main carriageway approach to the house. The landscape has long since been remodelled and the carriageway had not survived

---

[21] housed at Surrey Heath Museum, Camberley

like the one at Felbridge. Over its route now lay Chobham Place Woods but when the researchers looked closely they found that some of the trees were in alignment. Remarkably, they were able to trace the original avenue right through the centre of the wood. They concluded that probably one file was of Scots Pine and the other of Beech (both fashionable at the time). Four ancient Beeches survive today, at the house end.

Also shown on the map is a second avenue at right angles to the first, crossing through one corner of today's woods, and it too can still be traced. This one appears to have been of Chestnuts, judging from surviving specimens. A management plan has been drawn up for the woods. Derelict trees have been removed, the old Chestnuts have been pollarded to try and reinvigorate and perpetuate them and new saplings have been planted in the gaps. Gradually the avenued landscape will regain some of its former appearance. What a welcome landmark the trees must have been to any visitor reaching the end of his endurance, in a carriage rattling out of London and jolting finally across the rutted desolation of the Chobham heathlands.

SCOTTISH VETERANS

France is likely to have been a major source of inspiration. There are certainly French connections with the veteran Chestnuts in Scotland, which was still a foreign country and not very open to English ideas. This was especially so when Elizabeth I considered England to be threatened by Mary Queen of Scots. Mary was brought up in the French court and maintained contacts with several Continental countries, so the debate over origins goes round in circles. Certainly the tree was held in esteem. To have one entailed importing it because Chestnuts may not have produced viable seed that far north. Mary's personal secretary and 'close companion' was the Italian David Rizzio and he got hold of a Chestnut tree. It's still alive, at Melville Castle at Dalkeith in Midlothian, where he is said to have planted it as testimony to his love for Mary - a love that got him murdered in 1566. The tree is thought to be 450 years old and is one of those with a 25 foot girth. Mary herself is reputed to have planted the one at Newport-on-Tay in Fife. It grows beside the ruined chapter house of Balmerino Abbey, where they have a different story: that it was planted by the monks 700 years ago. That's for tourists, not for the National Trust for Scotland, which had the tree tested. It's 400-435 years old, so it was planted in Mary's lifetime. It looks that old too, having lost its main central trunk to laterals. The most important Chestnut connection with Mary is of national importance, for being the earliest that can be dated by document. It's older than those at Greenwich. It was planted in 1550 according to the estate records of Strathpeffer, in the Highlands. That was the seat of the Clan of MacKenzie and home to the Chief of the Clan. He was John MacKenzie, 9th Chief of Kintail and Privy Councillor to King James V and Mary Queen of Scots. The largest girth in Scotland belongs to the Cockcairnie Chestnut at Aberdour, Fife, at 29 feet. That too is considered to be 450 years old and like so many veterans has suffered die-back to become "a rather short, dumpy tree with a vast pot-bellied trunk." Also a bit decrepit is another of that age (25ft 4in), in the woods near the Rosslyn Chapel at Roslin, Midlothian. Old Chestnuts are scattered all over Scotland, even in the grounds of Glasgow Zoo (formerly Calderpark). In 2002 a shortlist of 100 Heritage Trees was compiled for Scotland and eight of them are Chestnuts. The Tree Council compiled a list of 50 'Great British Trees' to commemorate the Golden Jubilee of Elizabeth II. Three of those are Chestnuts (Tortworth, Croft and Bewdley).

COMMEMORATIONS

Commemorations are a problem when they are historic and undocumented. People have loved to attribute an old tree to a particular event or person, leaving us today with no idea whether it is true or not. Modern examples are easier to authenticate. At Swindon, in Wiltshire, Thamesdown Borough Council chose a Chestnut to commemorate Percy William who was one of the British Volunteers in the Spanish Civil War, killed at Caspe in 1938. The new National Arboretum in Staffordshire has them too although the great Chestnut Avenue that has been planted as the police memorial is of *Horse* Chestnut but there is one Sweet Chestnut on site with more planned. *(info courtesy of David Childs, Founder)*

The jackdaw is ancestrally a bird of the open grasslands, rather than woodlands, and chattering flocks still frequent the old pastures in the parks. They feed on a wide variety of food from seeds to snails, flies to moths. In particular they are adept at flipping over cow pats to see if there's anything tasty underneath. A greater accomplishment is having learnt how to prize open the autumn burs and take the chestnuts while they are still attached to the tree. No other bird in Britain has been recorded doing this. All the other wildlife has to wait until the fruits fall naturally. Jackdaws stay communal for breeding and nest in the holes of mature trees, delighted that Capability Brown left clumps of Oaks and Chestnuts that will house the whole flock.

THE AMAZING WORLD OF TANNINS

WHAT ARE TANNINS?

The cup of tea on the side here owes much of its appeal to the tannins in it. They are natural compounds produced by plants all round the world, whatever the climate or soil. In young plant growth they are to be found floating around in the vacuoles of the cells but as these cells age and lose much of their content so the tannins get absorbed into the cell walls. Eventually, the concentrations are so high they are viable for man to exploit.

Tannins are large molecules and are as complex and variable as the plants that produce them. Science is still working towards a better understanding of them. The poorest producers are the mosses, algae and fungi, which have very little, while the richest producers are usually trees. Even a single species will produce a complex of tannins, so that a Chestnut, for example, produces tannins in its young leaves that differ from those in its old leaves. For most trees the greatest concentrations are in their bark but tannins will be present throughout the plant, from the roots to the buds.

Plants produce tannins as part of their defence mechanisms, primarily to protect themselves from fungal and bacterial attack. But they can also protect the foliage from being eaten, whether by caterpillars or large mammals. They also guard developing fruits from being taken until the seed inside is viable. Any reader who has bitten into an unripe plum will have experienced, and remembered, the extreme astringent effects of the tannins as they drew your cheeks in! Upon ripening, the tannin level in most fruits drops, so that the fruit is palatable and will be carried off, dispersing the seed inside. The familiar dark brown outer skin of the Chestnut fruit contains 7-9% tannins.

They get their name from the Celtic word 'tan' for reddish brown and it is the tannins that give a cup of tea its colour - and its capacity to stain! Specifically, tannins are large molecules with pronounced astringent qualities, which means they draw liquid out of cells. That can be exploited to help close and heal wounds (as in treatments for acne) and in simple first aid for wasp stings - chew up a Chestnut leaf and apply the pulp to the sting. It will draw out the poisons. It is the action crucial to tanning hides into leather - kill off the bacteria before the hide decays, draw out moisture and close the pores. It's the magic recipe for anti-ageing creams too! The commercial applications are increasing all the time as so much scientific research is currently focused upon them.

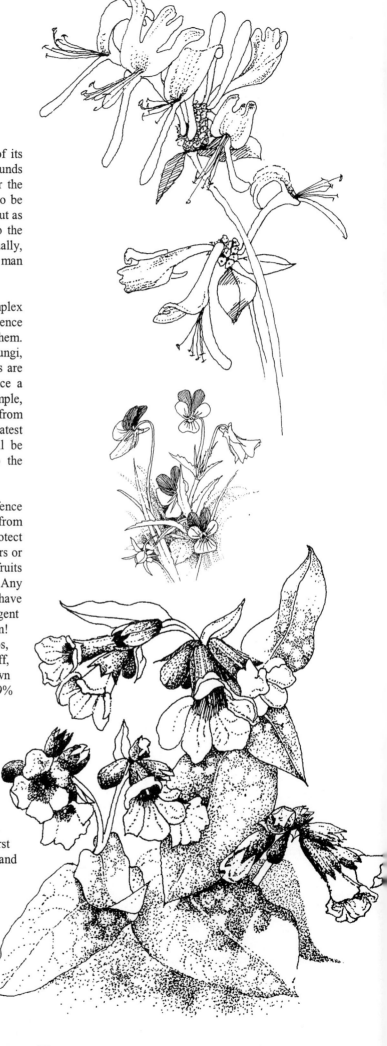

ENTER THE SWEET CHESTNUT

The 19th century was an incredible age for the way so many people began to explore their observations of the world around them in new 'scientific' ways. In France, at Lyons, a chemist called Michel noted with curiosity the way in which the chestnut stakes of his fence became stained black after rain where they were in contact with metal. That was about 1820 and his investigation of this phenomenon led to the commercial production of Chestnut tannins and started a major world industry. It led him to develop the system whereby the wood is chipped, heated in water, and the resulting decoction concentrated down into 'chestnut extract'. That was significant in the development of 19th century technology and of course the first tannin extract to be produced commercially in the world. In France by 1866 there was just the one factory but within thirty years there were over forty, producing 100,000 tonnes of extract. It took 34,000 tons of wood to produce 8,500 tons of extract.

It was boom time, with factory owners sending out agents to procure Chestnut timber. Many landowners sold off their nut orchards, which thereby changed the local economy. People with just a few trees were lured to sell those for a very low price just to get some extra money at all, while others were cutting too much too often for the natural cycle of regeneration. The French industry started to go into sharp decline, worsened by outbreaks of the Chestnut Bark Disease ('maladie de l'encre') and then the need for firewood during the wars.

The application was firstly as a dye in the silk industry, to give a fine blue-black colour. It was fast and even, and increased the weight of the silk, which was an advantage. Michel also experimented with using the chipped wood as a substitute for Oak bark in the tanning of hides and some fifty years later another pioneer, Koch, turned to using the extract rather than the raw wood chips. His usage was soon restricted to tanning heavy hides for industrial leather since it was not important with those that the extract left stains. Then in 1878 a method of removing the staining matter was discovered by Gondola and so the extract came into more general use.

That's the European history. Another history was unfolding simultaneously in America. In 1819 the *American Journal of Science* published William Sheldon's 'Application of Chestnut Wood to the Arts of Tanning and Dyeing'. He was not only enthusiastic about the results but revealed economic advantages too. He claimed Chestnut bark contained twice as much tannin as the Oak bark used traditionally by the tanners but it was to be many years before Chestnut was used extensively in America. There they exploited the native American Chestnut, *Castanea dentata* until Chestnut Blight ravaged the country in the 20th century.

While all this was going on abroad, the British had long been using Chestnut bark. That was by the tanners, who had found that it works faster than Oak bark. The resulting leather, however, was considered inferior. That of course would depend partly upon the care and time taken by the tanner and the purpose to which the leather was later put. As science explored these amazing compounds so other industries began to exploit them. By the 1980s Chestnut tannin came third on the list of natural tannins used in the UK. We were importing 2,500 tonnes, mainly from France and Italy, since supplies from America (from *Castanea dentata*) had dried up in the 1950s due to the blight epidemic.[1] The tannins are marketed in both solid and liquid form. The solid form is either a powder or a block, of which some 56-76% is tannin (with about 5.5-9.5% of non-tannins). The liquid form has only 29-49% tannin (and 5-10 % non-tan).[2]

[1] Lewington p.61
[2] Howes 147

The Raw Material[3]

All parts of the Chestnut tree contain tannins, even the dried prickly husk of the fruit contains 10-13%. The fallen leaves in autumn are another rich source and have been considered for commercial extraction but the prime source is the wood. The heartwood contains more than the sapwood but as it is so difficult to distinguish one from the other in Chestnut that the whole lot goes into the processing. It will contain about 7-8% tannins in northern Europe but 10-13% (and more) in southern Europe. That's because the tannins are produced as a defence against pathogens, which flourish in a long hot summer, and so the tree has to increase its defences. Trees on mountain sides, enjoying the full effects of the sun, produce more than those down on the plains. Decaying wood loses its tannins and gains stubborn colorants so is rejected from the extraction processes. That said, the Americans made full use of their Chestnuts killed by the blight epidemic, so that, in the 1930s for example, they took over 100,000 tons of tannins from the dead trees, especially in Pennsylvania.

The bark, as the first line of the tree's defence, has even higher percentages, averaging about 10% in the northern countries. The bark, however, is stripped off the wood and not used because it contains darker colorants and over four times as much sugar. The sugars adversely affect the extract and are difficult to deal with because they dissolve in water and therefore do not end up in the waste of 'non-tans'. One of the advantages of using Chestnut over other timbers is the low level of soluble non-tans it contains. The bark need not be wasted. It can go to those tanners who use the bark system rather than extracts, and therefore replace, or be mixed with, the usual Oak. It will of course affect the processing and the end result.

The age of the tree is also significant. Young trees try to outstrip their pathogens but as they age so they build up defences. When the tree is some 30 years old it is considered worth cropping for tannins. That's twice as long as the 15-year rotation popular in English coppicing and this extra delay in a financial return from the land has usually militated against cropping for this market. That said, there have been occasions when younger trees have been tested and found to contain just as much tannin. It is a very variable crop. Trees aged 50-70 years are considered the prime material but England hasn't supported large woodlands of Chestnut on such a slow rotation for this to be part of our silviculture. The increase in tannins from 30 to 50 years can be slight and maybe not worth the wait. France had to face that dilemma in the latter part of the 19th century when their Chestnut Extract industry was expanding rapidly and mature trees being mass felled, depriving whole areas of their very valuable nut harvest.

Off to the Works

Extracting the tannins from the wood is a factory process rather than a woodland craft.[4] Consequently it often took place miles from the woodlands, so long as there was a railway link for ease of transport, plus a good water supply and a ready workforce. In the early days (late 19th century) the timber would have been cut into lengths ready to go into a powerful machine that basically rasped the wood down into little chips. Any lengths that had too great a diameter for the machine were split through until they would fit. Soon more powerful machines were developed that would take larger sizes to reduce this work of splitting. So factories being set up in the 1930s installed machines that took massive trunks up to 10 feet in circumference and 11 feet 6 inches long. They were fed into a revolving drum armed with cutting blades, alternating smooth and serrated. These savaged chips off the end grain, so as to cut across as many cells as possible, to allow them to spill out their tannins. It was like a giant pencil-sharpener and was known at Boddington, for example, as the 'hogger'. It made an almighty row! It could be heard a couple of miles away, night and day, as shifts of workers kept the factory running continuously but that was a matter of local pride rather than cause for complaint.

Next, the chips passed through a succession of large wooden or copper vats to be treated with hot water (70ºC) to leach out the tannins. Some places boiled the chips while others subjected them to steam pressure but one way or another they ended up steeping in a vat for twenty four hours to leach out all the available tannins. The liquor was then pumped into more tanks where it was

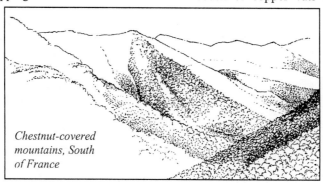

Chestnut-covered mountains, South of France

---

[3] section based on Howes, pp 139-43

[4] section based on Howes; and Ferrell, John, *Becoming Boddington*.

separated from the sludge, and then filtered, before going on to have the water content evaporated off to leave the dried extract - every 100 tons of wood yielded about 8.5 tons of solid extract with a 60-63% tannin content. It should be added, perhaps, that the technology involved in this processing was part of a much broader scene; you would have experienced much the same when touring a sugar factory for example.

Producing Chestnut Extract was big business in those European countries, such as France and Italy, where the tree was abundant. Through this availability grew a parallel demand for the product from a variety of industries. The commercial production of the tannins became an astonishing boom industry on the Continent through the latter part of the 19th century and into the beginning of the 20th century. This was true also of the United States, using their own *Castanea dentata*. It was not so in Britain. Before the Second World War, Italy was still practising vegetable tanning on a large scale and 95% of it was Chestnut whereas at the same time only 2-3% was being used in the United Kingdom. Our Chestnuts were being exploited by the hop-growers and fence-makers.

Finally, the waste of wood chips after the tannins have been extracted was not waste at all but was used to fuel the furnaces. It has been used also for briquettes, charcoal and the manufacture of wood alcohol. As for the 'waste' colorants, "the methods used by different factories for decolourizing the extract are said to be largely kept secret."[5] Some of it was used for dyes.

TANNINS AT WORK

Making Leather
The early civilisations learned how to tan hides and references occur in texts from the Assyrians, Greeks (Homer's *Iliad*) and the Egyptians. There is even an illustration of it on an Egyptian tomb painting, dating from 3000 BCE, and archaeologists have found other evidence from two thousand years before that - quite amazing considering it is such a long, slow and complicated process. It is not known when the techniques spread across the Mediterranean to the European side but certainly by 1500 BCE.[6] Today it is still a major industry and one with a future, since no synthetic material can match its special qualities.

The earliest tanners would have used the vegetable tanning process, still in use today. They had another method also, called 'tawing', which used minerals such as alum. Mineral tanning is now the commonest method in use but the alum has been exchanged for chrome salts, which tan in only a few hours, whereas vegetable tannins take weeks. This mineral process was known by 1856 but was not patented until 1884, in

[5] Howes; 147
[6] modern archaeology is pushing dates back all the time.

ALTERNATIVE SOURCES OF VEGETABLE TANNINS

MIMOSA is a name given not only to members of the genus *Mimosa* but to some species of *Acacia* too. Mimosa bark for tanning comes primarily from Black Wattle, *Acacia mearnsii*, (one of the 'Mimosas' sold in our florists for its ferny leaves and masses of pompom yellow flowers). Originally from Australia, it was introduced into South Africa about 150 years ago and is now cropped heavily in several southern African countries, as it is in Brazil and Sri Lanka. It yields not only tannins (30-40%) but also raw materials for the paper, plastics and textile industries.

the United States, by Augustus Schultz. Modern science has now taken this further by developing artificial agents called 'syntans'. To complete the overall picture, there is yet another process called 'oil tanning' or 'chamoising' to produce chamois leather (also known as shamoy and shammy leather) whereby the hides have fats rubbed into them and then they are hung up to dry. It is soft, very absorbent, and usually napped on both sides. In Britain it is best known perhaps as the shammy leather used in car cleaning. It is also the method used by Native Americans to produce their famous white buckskin clothing, warm and comfortable and soon adopted by the European colonists. Today the ancient system of vegetable tanning is in sharp decline - only 10-15% of leather is produced this way. The last tannery to use it in the United States closed down in 2001, when there were just three sites left in the United Kingdom.[7]

What Tannins do to Hides
As soon as the hide is removed from the carcass it comes under attack from bacteria and fungi and will decompose rapidly if not treated. That is why tanneries and slaughter-houses were often combined. The tanning process exploits the capacity of the tannins to draw out moisture and close tissue. Specifically, the molecules bond with the protein in the hide, called collagen, and produce cross-linked fibres that make hide insoluble and therefore no longer susceptible to attack. Thus from the tanners' point of view any tannin they use must be one that produces this cross-linked effect. Of those that do, some are still rejected because they have undesirable

[7] Info courtesy the International Council of Tanners

ALTERNATIVE SOURCES OF VEGETABLE TANNINS

VALONEA is the commercial name for tannins extracted from the acorn cups of those Oaks known as Valoneas, such as *Quercus aegilops* in Turkey and *Quercus graeca* in Greece. They all grow in the Eastern Mediterranean and get referred to in the Bible (e.g. Hosea 4:13). The extract, a pyrogallol, is used for high grade and heavy leathers, that need to be weight and water resistant. This is due to the content of ellagitannic acid giving the leather 'bloom'.

colour properties etc. The usual story from everyday life to illustrate this, is the bonding that is said to occur in a cup of tea, when the tannins bond with the proteins in the milk rather than with those in our livers and kidneys. However, this doesn't seem to have been proven scientifically

Tanners work with two types of tannins, which are known as catechols and pyrogallols. The catechols or 'condensed' tannins act fastest because they are the more astringent. They colour the leather from pink through the reds to browns (due to them having 'reds' or phlobaphenes) but will develop greenish-black discoloration if in contact with iron. They also oxidise out, reducing the lasting qualities of the leather. Trees used commercially for this type of tannin are usually Alder, Birch, Mimosa, Quebracho, and some conifers, such as Hemlock.

The pyrogallols or 'hydrolysable' tannins produce lighter coloured leathers because they deposit pale sediments of elegiac acid, called 'bloom'. This is advantageous. It increases the solidarity of the leather so that it wears better and makes it more waterproof - ideal leather for the soles of our shoes. It's also used for upholstery. Contact with iron, however, will still cause discoloration but this time it is bluish-black. In contrast to the catechols, they do not oxidise out. Trees used commercially for these tannins include the Sumac and Chestnut. Through history the tree that has been exploited greatly by tanners is the Oak because it contains tannins of both types.

A great skill of the tanner is knowing how to blend these two types of tannins to get just the right sort of leather for the intended purpose. One of the main problems is timing. From an economic viewpoint the tanner wants the job done as fast as possible but with thick hides there is the danger that the outside layers tan fast and become waterproof so that the tannins cannot continue to soak through to the deeper inner layers which remain untreated. Obviously if a whole hide is being treated great skill is required since the animal grew its hide in different thicknesses around its body.

Chestnut Extract

This pyrogallol tannin has great versatility and can be used in conjunction with all other tannins, including syntans. It can be used in the initial stages of the process or in any final retanning. Thus it works well in all modern methods of rapid tanning and tanners find it easy to use. With skill, they can fine-tune the mixtures and processing to get exactly the desired result. It works readily, for example, in conjunction with Quebracho and without the need for heating, although it works just as well in warm mixtures. It is naturally slightly acid and this is important in getting a good fixation onto the proteins. Thus it gives a high degree of tannage, of good substance and well-filled. The leather has high tensile strength, a high resistance to water and to wear. The degree of flexibility can be controlled by the processing according to the desired ends.

If used on its own Chestnut tannin can give the leather an undesirable reddish colour and this is one of the main reasons why it is so often used in conjunction with other tannins, such as those from Quebracho, Mimosa, Myrabolans, and valonia. The extract will contain non-tans but not so many as to be a problem or to make it uneconomic. These are almost entirely organic, which is important since some metals, like copper and iron, affect the leather. Nowadays, with the use of stainless steel vats, the content of copper and iron salts is so low as to have no appreciable effect.

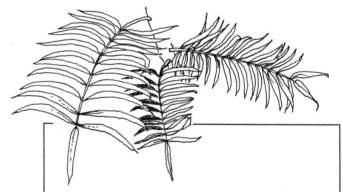

ALTERNATIVE SOURCES OF VEGETABLE TANNINS

QUEBRACHO is the name of several tree species of the genus *Schinopsis*, which belong to the family Anacardiaceae, as does the Cashew Nut. They grow in the Chaco of Argentina, Paraguay, and Brazil, where they are harvested from the wild. Stocks have been seriously depleted and are not readily replaced as the tree grows so slowly, taking up to eighty years to reach maturity. The decline is hastened by grazing cattle devouring the seedlings. The tannins (20-40%) are extracted from the heartwood, which is so hard it breaks the teeth of the power saws. When the tannins were more readily available they were the world's most important but industry now has to employ alternatives, primarily 'Mimosa bark'. The virtue of Quebracho is that it is fast acting and suitable for thick leather such as sole leather.

ALTERNATIVE SOURCES OF VEGETABLE TANNINS

MYRABOLANS are Indian trees belonging to the genus *Terminalia,* especially *T. chebula.* It is the dried fruits that are used commercially for tannins and a good yield would be about 32% but it is marketed in various grades. These are called 'myrabs' by the tanners, who use them to get a soft leather but they can be mixed with other tannins for a variety of leather types.

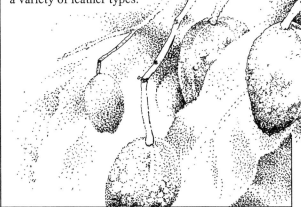

THE LEATHER AT WORK

If the task demands the leather to be thick and durable then Chestnut-tanned, or part tanned, would be considered, as in luggage, belts, straps, harness, and soles of footwear.[8] Additional virtue is found in chestnut leather's resistance to stretching. The advent of cars sported a huge demand for non-stretch leather, for seats. Nobody wanted to sit on wrinkles. The early motoring magazines were thick with big advertisements from the leather industry and the magazines must have derived considerable revenue from them. That usage survives today for the most expensive models but for a different reason. It now resolves temperature problems. If the expensive models are bought for use in the Middle East then the leather has to withstand the burning heat of the sun blazing through the windscreen and Chestnut can withstand that. It was a major market in Britain but during the production of this book, the cheaper prices from Asia finally took their toll and major companies like J. J. Williamson & Sons (Canterbury) Ltd. were forced out of business. The company was very helpful to us in the researches, as were J. Hewit & Sons Ltd, when contacted about leather bookbinding. They were granted the Royal Warrant for the manufacture of leather, in 1975, and bookbinding leathers are one of their specialities. Roger Barlee soon scotched the notion that Chestnut tanned leather is important for bookbinding, despite the number of times it gets listed for this purpose. Its qualities sound ideal, especially as it has a "good all-round feel to it" but it is not colour fast. Leather bindings are expensive so faded spines are not desirable. It has to be dyed and that relegates it to the cheaper range of bindings.

___
[8] shoe uppers are made with chrome alum

THE VEGETABLE TANNIN PROCESS

This can vary considerably according to the type of hide used and the sort of leather required but in principle runs as follows:-

(1) CURING - immediately upon removal the hide is salted and/or dried by either:-
Wet-Salting, when the hides are salted and stacked together for a month for the salt to penetrate the lot.
Brine-curing, when the hides aren't stacked but are carefully soaked in salt and disinfectant in a vat where total penetration occurs within 10-16 hours. This is the fastest and commonest method.

(2) SOAKING - in water for hours or several days to help remove salt, dirt, debris, blood and excess animal fats.

(3) FLESH REMOVAL by a machine nowadays.

(4) HAIR REMOVAL by soaking in a vat of limewater for 1-10 days after which a machine removes the hair.

(5) SCUDDING - the removal of anything from hair to fat that has been missed by machines. This is done by hand with a blunt knife or plastic tool.

(6) DE-LIMING in a vat of acid after which enzymes are added to prepare the surface and texture of the hide for tanning.

(7) TANNING - hides, on large frames, are passed through a series of vats containing the tannin solutions in increasing strengths.

(8) BLEACHING and DYEING PROCESSES for desired colours and the leather can also be soaked in oils, soaps, greases and waxes to make them more pliable, all depending upon the desired end result.

(9) ROLLING by machine to firm the leather to make it stronger.

(10) STRETCHING and DRYING in conditions of controlled heat.

(11) FINISHING - brushing chemical compounds into the grain side of the leather. Any imperfections still visible can be removed by buffing and abrasion; persistent buffing produces suede. Lastly, colours, waxes, oils etc. can be added to suit the customer's requirements.

Another major market for non-stretch leather was in harnessing for work horses - miles and miles and miles of it again. There was more in use than we might imagine at first because we are likely to forget the pit ponies working in the mines. They proliferated when parliament outlawed the use of women as hauliers, in 1842. By 1913 there were over 70,000 pit ponies, after which date they declined. More horses were employed in the marshalling yards of the railway companies, as quick easy ways of getting power to trucks for shunting. More could be seen at docks, quays, and the canal system; it wasn't just a matter of ploughing fields or drawing carts and buses. The internal combustion engine replaced most during the first half of the 20th century but not all. There is currently a revival so that today there are over 10,000 heavy horses in the country. Additionally there are cross-breeds or 'vanners' plus native breeds that work, such as the Cobs, Dales and Fell ponies. Even elephants are harnessed by Britain! Overall, the demand for harness leather is flourishing but primarily nowadays for the equestrian market.

More leather worked as machine belts, to link the looms etc. to their overhead power source, in mills and factories. These must not stretch and become slack, else efficiency would be lost. Production was lost altogether if the machine had to be stopped for a belt to be replaced. Goodness knows how many miles of such belts were in use at any one time during the great age of steam! Today, there is only one steam mill still operating in the UK, albeit mainly as a museum, and that is the Queen Street Mill at Burnley. The illustration opposite was drawn about 1981, of the belt driven flour-sieving system in Coxes Lock Mill, Addlestone, Surrey. It had never been modernised because it worked so efficiently. It was unbelievably quiet; just the sound of falling flour like snow through the trees. It sieved over sixty tons of flour a week. However, within a few months the enterprise changed hands and the new owners closed it down and destroyed everything. Only part of the mill pond and the main mill building were saved (now apartments).

VISIT TO A TANNERY

Chesterfield is a medieval market town in Derbyshire, retaining some of its old buildings such as the open-sided market hall and the parish church with its famous twisted spire. Like other towns in the North Midlands it has since had its industrial developments, especially with the coming of the railways. Thus, down by the station, was founded the tannery of Joseph Clayton and Sons. Now over a hundred years old, it is still working and still uses vegetable tannins. Indeed it is one of only three in the country that does.

Externally it is another gaunt industrial block of red brick but of course the interior reveals this place is rather special. The ground floor is chequered with pits of tanning fluid, overlaid with the top rails of the frames from which the hides are suspended. There are different strengths of fluid in different pits and the workmen move the hides along from strongest to weakest. This is likely to be every day for six weeks but depends partly upon the final colour required. As the hides are removed from a pit so its fluid level drops and is topped up with water. Thus the mixture in each pit does not stay the same strength. Beyond the pits, against the wall, is a line of great drums, rotating at about twenty times a minute. These impress extra fluid into the hides to deepen their colours. Hides stay on the drums, night and day, for about three weeks. These scenes have remained unchanged for generations, save for legal imposition of safety fencing. All around is the inevitable smell of leather, tinged with acid, and an unexpected smell and taste in the back of your throat, of bitter chocolate. That comes from the chestnut tannins that can be added to the fluids.

If this tannery were using Oak then it would be a very slow process indeed. Instead, the process is hastened, by using a mixture of Chestnut and other vegetable tannins. The Chestnut is imported as powder from Slovenia. Made as an aqueous extract, it has been concentrated, by spray-drying, to a balance of 60% tans and 40% non-tans. Among the non-tans are compounds that give the powder its wonderful rich gold colour (pure tannins are whitish). The tannery does not use this pure but incorporates it in its own mixtures. Typically, their standard final mix is 25% Quebracho, 25% Chestnut and 50% Mimosa. You know when the Mimosa is being used because it puts a sweet smell in the air. The mix thus combines both catechol and pyrogallol tannins. Sodium sulphite is added to 'sweeten' the Chestnut to reduce its acidity.[9] That's to reduce the risk of it fixing the outer layers of the hide before the inner, which would produce brittle leather, liable to "snap like a biscuit" and not withstand the mechanical stresses that take place during the processing.

Moving through the upper floors is to pass between stacks and stacks of leather, each some four feet high. Again there seems to be little concession to modernity, save for the forklift truck! This is a modern business though, surviving in a highly competitive world. Up until about fifteen years ago, their leather was primarily for industrial use. Many readers will have encountered it - remember the hinges on the old red telephone boxes

and the straps for adjusting windows on the trains? Nowadays much of it goes for equestrian leatherwear, and gets exported all round the world - from the United States to Australia and Japan.[10]

---

[9] This addition of sodium sulphite increases the proportion of 'non-tans'.

[10] with thanks to Matthew Abbott at Joseph Clayton and Sons for permitting the visit, and to Barry North for going and recording the material for this section.

Looking across the floor of tanning pits to one of the drums, at Joseph Clayton and Sons.

TO THE LEATHER FINISHERS

Although there are so few tanners left in Britain who work the Chestnut tannins, the industry has left craftsmen experienced in the skills of finishing the leather, working for specialist companies. Thus on the hottest day on record we braved the joys of the M1 to accept an invitation to visit the Metropololitan Leather Co. Ltd. at Thrapston in Northamptonshire. It's an old stone-built village in the valley of the River Nene, amid miles of rumpled cornfields. Round behind the fire station is a small industrial estate with the long low modern building that we wanted - a great contrast to the grimy baulk of the tannery.

John Houghton showed us round and shared his forty years experience. He can just look at piece of leather and know how it was tanned. On entering, there is the expected smell of fresh leather from the stacks all around - stacks at different stages in its processing, leather from different animals, leather tanned in different ways. The pale stacks were still in their fresh state whereas the dark brown leather had been through the dyeing processes. The Chestnut stack had been imported from Spain, but it might just as easily have come from Italy or as far as Mexico. The sheets are still recognisable in shape as animal hides and these will be selected to fit a client's requirements, because there are differences in thickness across the hide. The great central section from the animal's back is tougher, with a different fibre, from that off the animal's belly. The back is the best for most jobs, the shoulder is second best and the underbelly is the crudest and not so good. Long lengths for straps, such as for horse-riding reins, are cut from the full length of the hide, from shoulder to tail. Shorter lengths, up to 60 inches, for bridle work, can be cut out of the shoulder sections. Broader shoulder sections serve for a wide variety of items from suitcases and brief cases, down to wallets. Not all shoulder leather is the same: it's likely to have 'growth lines' (wrinkles) to accommodate the movement of the animal's head, so leather without this is dearer. However, leather showing the growth lines is currently fashionable.

The trade in leatherwear for horses has declined very sharply in terms of working horses, but there has been a compensatory rise from the increase in equestrianism. Similarly, camel racing has become big business, so here they prepare the Spanish leather ready for export to Danish manufacturers who produce the saddles etc. and export them to the Middle East. Presumably the saddle leather travels further before it is raced than it does afterwards, jested John Houghton as he turned to the next stack. They were destined for a different but important outlet, the fashion houses. They are very desirous of English leather, especially those catering for the Japanese and American markets. Off another stack he held up half a hide to explain that another expanding outlet was the furniture trade. British leather is in demand for table tops etc. Having been tanned in Britain, it would be finished at Thrapston and then go to the furniture maker who has it dyed according to specification. Over his forty years in the business John Houghton has seen many shifts in demand from one purpose to another. Currently there were some new outlets due to the sharp decline of the industry in countries like the United States, so that we now prepare the leather for the handgun holsters of FBI and CIA agents. A new and large growth market for non-stretch leather, which took them a little by surprise, is the sex industry.

A stack of Asian goatskin had been chrome tanned for use by industry for diaphragms. Obviously it can't have holes in it so part of the processing is to hold it up to a light in a darkroom. After cutting out, any wastage is then cut for medical needs - small pieces for finger stalls, larger pieces for the construction of artificial limbs. Chrome leather is much used for medical needs because it is softer and more elastic but obviously for some purposes non-stretch Chestnut leather is essential. Orthotists confirmed this, and discussed individual examples, but their suppliers of medical leather would not co-operate, to give us an overall view of the subject.

Ultimately there is hardly any waste from this industry, since artist-craftsmen take small pieces and Hell's Angels arrive for bigger bits! Taking the industry as a whole, it has been 'decimated' in the last few years by cheaper products from the Third World. At the same time, some industries have turned back to vegetable tanned leathers because their consumers are worried about the use of certain minerals becoming undesirable contaminants. Manufacturers themselves set targets for the percentage of their product that is organic or able to be recycled. That ought to be good news for the Chestnut but the process is too slow and the quicker, cheaper, alternatives are developing instead.

DRILLING MUDS

Tannins even go to sea! They are used in the drilling industry, whether it is for oil, gas or water, since the problems are the same. Namely, how to prevent the drilling head becoming over-heated, corroded, or clogged with the debris being drilled out. To overcome this: 'drilling fluids' are pumped down the shaft, to cool and clean. As they flow back to the surface they bring the heated debris with them. To avoid clogging, various additives have been tried, including tannins. They reduce the viscosity and thereby increase fluidity to act as an effective dispersant but they require high levels of alkalinity (pH 10.5-11.5) in order to solubilise them into maximum effectiveness. The alkalinity combats corrosion.

The industry started exploring tannins back in the 1930s and turned initially to South America's Quebracho trees as the richest source. Difficulties in supply led to the use of Quebracho extracts: a prime compound is sulphomethylated quebracho, formed from a reaction with caustic soda, formaldehyde and sodium bisulphite. It is more water soluble and can be complexed by chromium and other metals to form stable complexes used as thinners in high temperature, water-based muds. Tannins from other trees have been used also, including the Chestnut.

It was during the 1950s to 1970s that Chestnut tannins had their main phase of use, running on into the 1980s. In America they continued in what are known as 'red muds'. In general Chestnut tannins passed out of general use as scientific investigations and developments produced new additives for the freshwater-based muds, which can be cheaper and more effective. These are known as lignosulphonates. Even some of these still contain Chestnut tannins in their recipe and also the tannins of the Quebracho trees.

Tannins were used originally when drilling land wells, rather than under the sea. Thus Britain missed out on that phase since our drilling industry rose to the fore c.1970-75 as an offshore industry, exploring the North Sea for gas and oil. Worldwide, the tannin manufacturers still receive orders from the drilling industry.

Although the tannins are effective as dispersants in this industry they can have the reverse effect also. Research in water purification has been trying to overcome the problem of fine matter passing right through the filtering systems. It has been found that adding Chestnut tannins caused some types of particles to 'flocculate' i.e. they bunched together in tufts, which made them big enough to be trapped. This principle is still being explored and developed by scientists today.

THE STEAM AGE

Mention steam and people minds are likely to turn to railways and locomotives. They are probably the most cherished aspects of our industrial heritage. Over 100,000 people visited the National Railway Museum at York in 2001, putting it in the top three of tourist attractions. It houses the largest collection of its kind in the world. If you were asked to guess how many steam railways are still operating in Britain you would probably think there were only a few. In fact there are 108, plus another 60 steam centres, distributed throughout Britain.[11] These attract nearly eight million visitors a year, who spend nearly £43 million. This is big business, not a weird little world of train-spotters.

It is of course only a glimpse into the past when Victorian enterprise strove for ever-increasing access, speed and reliability. It's with the last two that Chestnut tannins played their part. The steam boiler systems of the locomotives suffered from corrosion as lime scale built up along the pipes, despite the addition of slaughterhouse waste. To deal with the sludge building up in the system, a valve was designed in the bottom, where it gathered. This could be opened so that the pressure would force out the sludge (an operation known as a 'blow-down') but this was inefficient since it meant losing heat, pressure and time. They tried adding tannins to the water and they worked wonders. Firstly, their action as oxygen scavengers denied oxygen to the crystallising processes of calcium carbonate, calcium sulphate, magnesium and silica, thereby inhibiting the build up of lime scale. In so doing, they acted as dispersal agents, keeping the minerals moving in the

---

[11] excellent map on the website of "UK Heritage Railways" which also has an absorbing page of 'Facts and Figures'

water instead of sinking as sludge. Tannins are still used this way today in steam locomotives. Not much is needed - 100 parts of tannins to every million parts of water. It degrades though, by reacting with the oxygen dissolved in the feed water that tops up the system. This is overcome by using a dosing pump that adds five parts per million into the head water (more if it is not high purity water).

Once these properties were known, industries were soon exploiting them. The first patent is believed to have been taken out in 1876, by a company called *Houseman and Thompson*. They had two working concerns, one in North East England and one in the North West. Their patent was for the use of "a greasy product of oriental extraction," for oxygen scavenging and sludge conditioning. It worked. Commercial pride being what it is, there is probably truth in the oral tradition of the company, that their product went to the Battle of Jutland (May 1916) twice - in the boiler systems of the British fleet and also in those of the German fleet.

The company monitored their product carefully, taking it to the Public Analyst at Newcastle-upon-Tyne at regular intervals - in 1912, 1915, 1930, and 1949, and on each occasion received a favourable report. Today, the product is still in commercial use.[12] It is not likely to be among the chemicals used in a domestic central heating system because the additive is whisky-coloured and would stain carpets if there were a spillage. However, it's going round in commercial steam boiler systems, ranging from those in hospitals to those in food factories. The main difference today is that the tannins are not simply of Chestnut but are a blend, primarily with those of Quebracho and Mimosa. Similarly, Chestnut tannins are not present in *all* the steam locomotives of today - there are 1,289 of them, of which about 700 are likely to be working at any one time. For example, one of the largest companies, the Severn Valley Steam Railway, uses Mimosa instead.[13]

Apart from locomotives, tannins in steam boilers feature in the histories of traction engines, steam ships, yachts and launches, steam dredgers and the factory boilers that powered the British industries that led the world.

THE SMUGGLERS TALE

Back in the 17th century drinking tea was restricted to the wealthier classes and in cities like London gave rise to special tea shops that were the precursor of the more famous coffee-houses. By 1700 there were several hundred tea shops in London and we were importing a million pounds of it every year. Prices were high (especially once a tea duty had been imposed) and were kept that way deliberately to ensure patronage was restricted to an approved clientele. Smugglers were soon undermining that but they needed the collusion of the people along their routes between their coastal havens and the London markets. People were 'rewarded' for not reporting the night rides and for stowing the wares out of sight during the daylight hours. The kegs were opened and a portion of tea set aside for them, to be replaced by an adulterant. The two commonest are said to have been the dried chopped leaves of Ash and Chestnut.

It was the widespread use of adulterants in an equally wide range of goods that was partly responsible for the founding of trading companies that endeavoured to try and guarantee quality. Thomas Twining started trading tea from The Strand in London in 1706. The Twining company still trades from the same site and holds the Royal Warrant. The degree of adulteration by the 19th century was rife and so was public discontent, which led to a proliferation of companies offering standardised recipes and ingredients, leading to sustained commercial success. Joseph and Edward Tetley founded their tea-trading partnership in 1837. In 1869 Brooke Bond Tea was founded by Arthur Brooke, and so on.

---

12 available, for example, from Accepta Ltd, product no. 2012
13 information kindly given by Michael Heintzman

Grow Your Own Heritage

THREE CONSIDERATIONS

Sweet Chestnuts are easy to grow providing the site is free draining. They die if their roots are in persistently wet soil. It was interesting to revisit a coppice known in childhood only to find that the majority of the stools had died. The water table had shifted, changing the places where springs emerged and water now seeps down through the coppice, killing the stools. It was decidedly boggy!

The second consideration is the alkalinity. They like acid conditions. They will tolerate a pH value up to 6 and often a bit above but not 7; there are, at the time of writing, some Internet pages reporting tolerance above this but they are not being received seriously by other scientists who regard the reported procedures as flawed. At the Agricultural Experiment Station in Connecticut they are busy conducting trials on alkalinity, to see if it might be a factor in disease resistance. No doubt a lot more than that will be observed at the same time and be published in due course. We have seen some Chestnuts growing on top of the chalk Downs but this proved to be misleading, since the chalk was overtopped by deposits of acidic clay-with-flints.

Thirdly, space must be taken into account. Remember that it is a big forest tree and therefore not suited to the size of suburban gardens. It can of course be pollarded or coppiced to keep it within limits but there are more attractive alternatives for small gardens. Managers of large spaces, such as parks, farms, recreation grounds, nature reserves, churchyards and cemeteries etc. might well consider it. For those places where something a little more decorative might be in order then the Dictionary of Gardening from the Royal Horticultural Society lists six cultivars that differ from the norm:- 'Asplenifolia' and 'Laciniata' both have narrow cut leaves, 'Albomarginata' has pale variegated edges to the leaves while 'Purpurea' has darker foliage. 'Heterophylla' is polymorphic while 'Holtii' has a narrow conical crown. Buying these is a different matter. An Internet search found listings only for the variegated and the purple but the nurseries reported that they did not hold stock. They reported that they would buy it in to satisfy an order but were not overly confident, at that time, of being successful. The Plantfinder listed no Sweet Chestnuts at all.

GROWING FROM SEED

Chestnuts grow readily from seed - the brown nuts. The scarcity of seedlings around Chestnut woods might lead you to think otherwise but that is due to the depredations of grey squirrels. They, plus other mammals and birds, clear the lot. Jays and squirrels bury hoards, which ought to mean some get left to germinate but practically every one gets found and consumed during the following winter. Gather your own nuts, choosing the plumpest and freshest, and sow them straight away before they can begin to dry out. Plant far more than you need because not all British seed is viable: out of 240 nuts about 175 will grow. If your only source is the supermarket food shelf then buy them right at the start of the season before they have suffered too much from

Jay. One of the species fond of Chestnuts and which aids its spread by flying off with nuts and burying them.

storage. Even so, plant extras. Any commercial seed compost will serve but avoid mushroom compost because it contains alkaline material. Plant at a depth to give at least 2cm of soil over the nut, using a full-depth pot, not a half-pot, and certainly not one with a water reservoir in the bottom. Beware not to over-water at all times: kindness kills. Plant one nut per pot and stand them outside for the winter, where nothing can impede drainage from the pots. Some nuts may germinate straight away and not survive the winter. Those that wait till spring do best. They will have been growing roots through the winter. Alternatively, plant them direct into the garden soil, in a place where they can be dug up for transplanting to their permanent site. In this case, there is a risk that mice will dig them up for lunch so cover the nuts with small-holed wire netting before covering them with soil. Think ahead - use a piece of mesh big enough to do the job but not so big as to be a hindrance during the transplanting, when it should be cut free of the sapling.

Growing them in the open ground is by far the best way because it gives the roots all the room they want and a good rooting system at this stage is essential: it has to last the tree a lifetime, which is going to be longer than yours! If pots are used, keep potting-on into larger pots before the roots get spiralled round. When they start to spiral it is difficult to stop them and when planted out you want the roots to spread widely to support the tree. In the second and subsequent pottings-on use a soil-based compost because peat is difficult to keep moist when the tree is planted out. They should be planted out at the end (autumn) of their first growing season and they will need protection from herbivores such as rabbits because they will still be less than half a metre high; a lot less in some cases.

SAPLINGS

Alternatively, you can buy a young tree ready to plant out. The International Register for Sweet Chestnut, on the Internet, lists in excess of 1,800 different cultivars. That's a staggering total, leaving no doubt that this really is "the most important nut in the world." The list is still growing, as hybridisation programmes continue. Getting one in Britain is not so easy, especially as there are international trade restrictions to reduce the risk of introducing virulent diseases from abroad. The majority of sales catalogues of trees did not offer this species at all. Most of the cultivars have been selected for their fruit, which does not affect their amenity value and the benefits for wildlife may be an additional asset. It is a reminder, however, to check the catalogues of fruit tree suppliers. The nation's most important is Ken Muir Ltd at Clacton, Essex. They have been offering Chestnut since 1999 but as sales are limited they are at the moment offering only one cultivar, the standard 'Marron de Lyon'. The Bluebell Nursery at Ashby de la Zouch, offers that one too. For a much wider choice, turn to the Agroforestry Research Trust at Dartington in Devon. Their catalogue lists seventeen cultivars and, very usefully, clarifies which will pollinate which for best fruit production. Although a single tree has both male and female flowers on it, they are not necessarily viable at the same time so cross-pollination is vital for fruiting. That said, you are still at the mercy of the weather, since warmth is crucial for fertilisation (27-30°C according to Crawford). Choosing good fruiting cultivars may be important when it comes to persuading those

Authorities that decree all tree plantings must be of native species, for the benefit of wildlife. A fruiting Chestnut becomes the Ritz for several weeks in the autumn! While looking at the catalogue from the Agroforestry Research Trust note that they offer the Hop cultivar 'Fuggle' that features elsewhere in this book - another important addition wherever there's an interest in growing culturally important plants. Also worth contacting is the Oakover Nursery at Charing near Ashford in Kent, which will supply wholesale.

PLANTING DENSITIES

Chestnuts are big forest trees so when it comes to planting one destined to be a fine specimen, choose somewhere with plenty of space. Take into account the sight-lines because it not only needs room to grow but also to show off its beauty and be admired. When it comes to planting screening trees, Chestnuts can be included among other species but if the screen is to be solely of Chestnut then more thought is required. If the aim is to block the view at eye level then coppice the Chestnut. If screening is required somewhat higher, then consider pollarding or leaving the trees to grow on naturally. The problem with coppice and pollard screens is that cutting opens up the view, so plant a double row, staggered, to be cut alternately. On sites where the aim is to screen a roadside car park there can be problems with some Authorities at the planning stage if the local police have asked that such

Grey Squirrels are common denizens of the fruiting Chestnut coppices, especially if Oaks are used as standards. They were introduced from North America in the 19th century.

screens be avoided. They obstruct the view of passing patrol cars, which might otherwise be able to spot the undesirable lurking with evil intent.

Restoring old coppices is straightforward since the original planting distances can be determined and copied. With new copses the density is important but there is no golden rule. Spacing depends upon the reason for the copse being planted. If it is for cropping then the end market must be determined beforehand so that the number of years in the cycle is known. For a seven year cycle plant 7-9 feet apart, which requires 600-800 saplings per acre. For a ten year cycle plant 9-10 feet apart, needing 500-600 saplings, while for a fifteen year cycle plant 11-12 feet apart, needing 300-400 saplings. Those are approximate figures based on the experiences of foresters consulted. Everyone had variations on these figures and the wisdom may well go back several generations. There is a new option now, where land is being set-aside for nature conservation but where maybe a return off the land would supplement much needed funds. Each situation will need judging separately. Bear in mind that a close-planted pure Chestnut coppice does not support a great wealth of other species, despite what you can read to the contrary. It suppresses virtually all the ground flora too. Better to think in terms of including Chestnut among other species. Leave the saplings to become established for a few years (five is popular), before cutting them down for the first time. The fellings can be sold to gardeners for stakes. Avoid the myth that trees should always be felled in the winter, preferably November to December. Chestnut is an exception. If you cut at that time the stools will sprout the following spring in time for the new growth to get hammered by late frosts. Leave the cutting to March, or even early April in sites prone to such frosts, and then new growth does not emerge until after the last frosts.

FUNGI

When planting out Chestnuts it can be beneficial to mix into the planting hole a sample of soil gathered from around the roots of established Chestnuts because this will almost certainly contain special soil fungi. Certain species attach themselves to the roots of specific plants where the two species work together for mutual reward (symbiosis). These can be very beneficial in poor soils and many of the plants of our dry sandy areas are believed to have them. That includes the Chestnut, although the fungal species involved in Britain are not fully understood. The coppices are poor places to hunt for toadstools in the autumn, so there are few clues as to which species are important. As a teenager I remember being shown how to find truffles, in an old bank that ran through the coppice. On the Continent a prime edible toadstool found under Chestnuts is the Cep or Penny Bun (Boletus edulis), which does

sometimes grow under Chestnut here, but more often under Beech. The white *Lactarius vellereus* turns up from time to time; if you break the cap it will bleed white 'milk' but it is not edible. Inedible also is Russula foetens, which has a white stem supporting a brown cap which can be quite slimy on occasions.

PESTS AND DISEASES

Fortunately, growing your own Chestnut heritage leaves you relatively free of many concerns under this heading - much safer than growing roses! However, a couple of diseases can be very nasty, if not fatal. Therefore, wherever Chestnuts are an important part of the landscape, managers should be aware of Ink Disease and Chestnut Blight, and protect young trees from rabbits (illus) etc. Ink Disease is caused by the fungi *Phytophthora cambivora* and *P. cinnamomi*, which live in the soil. They attack the root tips and progress unseen up the root to the base of the trunk, causing die-back in the crown of the tree. Eventually wounds open up at the base of the trunk, which bleed black 'ink'. By this stage the disease is likely to be fatal but some trees fight off an attack by growing barriers of cork to isolate the attack. These fungi like moisture, especially on heavier soils, so if the Chestnuts are growing in their preferred free draining sandy soils there should be no problem. Where there is a concern, then investigate acquiring one of the disease-resistant hybrids and cultivars, or stock that has been inoculated with a combatant fungus.

Chestnut Blight is serious. It is caused by the parasitic fungus *Cryphonectria parasitica* (syn. *Endothia parasitica*), which reached epidemic proportions in the United States and wiped out their Chestnuts through the first half of the 20th century (like our Dutch Elm Disease). Then it appeared in Italy in 1938 and has now spread to all Chestnut growing areas except Brittany and Britain. Climate change is expected to suit it and so there is an expectation that it is only a matter of time before something like a migrating bird carries the spores over the Channel. Protective measures, in terms of treatments and disease resistant Chestnuts, are being investigated and developed around the world. Hopefully then, we have learnt from the epidemic of Dutch Elm Disease in the 1970s and will act promptly and effectively if our Chestnut heritage comes under threat.

Just three insects can make a nuisance of themselves: Chestnut Moth (*Pammene juliana* syn. *P.* fascina), Chestnut Codling Moth (*Lespeyresia splendana*), Chestnut Weevil (*Balaninus elephas* syn. *Curculio elephas*, but these are really only of major concern in orchards. As there has been no history of such nut orchards in Britain the topic is not included in this study. Anyone interested will find essential details in Martin Crawford's handbook from The Agroforestry Trust.

AND NOT FORGETTING...

The files have still got lots of material that has not been included in the final text, for a variety of reasons. It ranges from castanets to the slatted wooden holders for litter bins, and log rolls at the garden centres. A number of industrial uses are still being developed.. The hoopers, and to a lesser extent the coopers, were significant users but have not been given detailed coverage as we unearthed neither fresh material, nor had a differing viewpoint, from that which is available in print already. The same is true of the hurdle-makers but so much of the original archive material we saw did not specify the tree. Here are another three pages from the remainder.

BOATBUILDING was one of the topics where more material might come to light with a more diligent search. Only a generation ago there were still dozens of boatyards sitting on the banks of the Thames, paddling their footings in the water, from say Kingston up to Staines. Nearly all of them have gone now and it's the same story all round the country. The main buildings have become yacht clubs, restaurants, art galleries and apartments or the sites redeveloped altogether. Such a wealth of skills has been lost for there are so many disciplines involved in building the range of crafts that these boatyards once produced so proudly. Apprenticeships are rare and even rarer are people keen to take them up. One survivor on the Thames is the yard of Michael Dennett, where the above study (unfinished) was made back in the 1980s.

Chestnut was used seldom but there *were* craftsmen who knew how to get it to satisfy their needs. They passed on their knowledge to people like Malcolm Adkins, up in the Midlands, at the Coventry Boatbuilders and Chandlery. He reported having built two boats with Chestnut planking and learning that, *"You have to be careful with it as it can get a nasty cross grain in places which snaps when putting in tight bends as at the front of the garboard (first) plank. That said it does have some comparisons with oak"*

"From personal experience I would regard this as an adequate timber for small boat planking - and it does have the advantage of being quite available. I am not sure that I would prefer it to a good larch, or pine, although it is quite decorative."[1]

The records from the Second World War show that Chestnut was pressed into service in the boatyards. In particular, minesweepers had to be of wood since metal would have created a magnetic field and detonated the mines. The favoured construction was of Oak with decking and deckhouse of Oregon Pine but as the War progressed so increasingly Oak had to

---

[1] pers.comm. Malcolm Adkins

be deployed for other purposes. Soon it was used only for the beams, frames, knees and shaft log. The rest had to be constructed from Douglas Fir, Elm, Larch - and Chestnut.[2]

Restorations of old craft are now using Chestnut occasionally. There was an example on the Internet relating to a Thames skiff, *Rowena*, which was given a new sternpost. The site comments that Chestnut is *"a very versatile timber."*

WALKING STICKS

The bold head of a cock pheasant, raised in alarm, converts readily to a carven image. At least, it does in the hands of a craftsman like John Marsh. He creates these as the heads of walking sticks, comfortably smoothed to suit the palm. He works right out on the fringes of Chestnut country, off the west coast of Scotland. The Isle of Mull is perhaps not the most obvious place to look for them, but John Marsh replied, *"yes, there is chestnut on the Isle of Mull. I harvest it myself. I find it grows from the main trunk outwards, then upwards, so that when cut it ends up hockey stick shape which must then be steamed straight. It does make very handsome straight shanks, much springier than hazel but equally as strong, with very knobbly features."*

John Marsh is one of dozens of stick-makers in the country; it was amazing how many came up on the Internet search. Thus in just a few minutes you can open up a whole world of little detailed sculptures. Many craftsmen portray subjects from everyday life, especially birds and animals, reminiscent of those found on medieval cathedral choir stalls and just as good - one of the unsung treasures of current British craftsmanship. Although their products are diverse, they all strive for a marriage between beauty and serviceability.

The notion of 'cane' is dominant in the United States, where they do not have the term 'walking stick'. In Britain 'cane' refers normally to a stick as a fashion accessory, which reflects their early history. They creep into British records during the

1400s and then rose in popularity once given approval by Henry VIII who had over forty of them. Most early examples were imported into Europe from the East, from places like Malaysia, since they were made from the 'canes' of Malacca, one of the Rattan Palms (*Calamus scipionum*). Today, over 200 different species worldwide are used for this product. They are highly finished, not just in terms of varnishing and polishing, but in the treatment given to the top. Some are simply smoothed and rounded, perhaps with an elegant silver finial, but the fashion today is for them to be carved. That's where craftsmen like John Marsh come in and there are probably several hundred craftsmen who produce these today. It's amazing there is enough demand but there is a wide range of product, from simple walking aids to elegant costume accessories, hiking staves and trekking poles, market sticks and thumb sticks, ski poles and wading poles, crooks and cleeks.[3]

There are two broad categories: sticks made entirely from one stave of wood and those where the handle has been added to the shaft. Even those with a sizeable curved-over handle can be made from one stave simply by using heat. The wood is plunged into sand, heated from below, until it becomes pliable. Then it is bent over and tied in position, or fixed in a mould, and left to cool. As it cools it hardens. It so doing it retains the shape. The elaborate scrolls known as 'shepherds' crooks' were different. Instead of being made from a cheap coppice stave they were carved out of a big block of wood, which was much more expensive. Then there was so much sawing, drilling and filing so that the price rose high. The market was soon undermined by cheap metal imitation scrolls that are now much sought after in their own right and are still made by blacksmiths today.

For sheer numbers though, there is no outlet to beat that of the National Health Service. The demand for walking sticks as mobility aids is phenomenal. The contract goes to just one company, the Phoenix Walking Stick Co. Ltd., at Nailsworth in Gloucestershire. Indeed, they are the only manufacturer of crook-handled

---

[2] House p.78

[3] cleek: Scottish for a large crook; not a golf club

walking sticks in the country. Each year they produce between 150,000 to 200,000 sticks, or, putting it another way, 128-170 miles of them if you put the initial straight staves end to end. The staves travel that far to reach the factory since they are grown on the Cowdray estates at Midhurst in West Sussex. The crop is cut, by hand with a machete, after three years, so although the Romans had little use but firewood for such material it certainly suits a need today. Each stick was once a living thing and is therefore individual, needing to be finished by hand, to ensure it reaches the British Standard awarded to this product (BS5181:1975). That makes it one of only two coppice products in Britain that has a British Standard and both are for Chestnut since the other is for paling fencing.

HONEY

Although Chestnut is a catkin-bearing tree designed for wind pollination, it also produces nectar for insect pollination. Bees feed on the pollen and gather the nectar for honey as their winter-feed. Some sources declare that Chestnut is only a nectar plant in Southern Europe but the British apiarists consulted said their bees did collect from British Chestnuts. They said the honey was 'tangy' and 'nutty' in flavour. Some did not like it at all and resented the nearby Chestnuts. There was dispute also as to whether bees collect honeydew from Chestnuts in this country. If they do, it doesn't seem to be very much. Chestnut honey is being used, among others, in current research into allergies.

MEDICINE

The tree is used little in medicine. The astringent qualities of the tannins means it can be used for haemorrhoids although there may be a degree of doubt over preventing them in the first place by carrying some nuts in a silk purse around the neck. Otherwise there have been various treatments, over several centuries, for respiratory problems, especially whooping cough. Chestnut is one of the Bach Flower Remedies and is used in homeopathy. The tannins are being investigated currently to discover their exact action and how it might be exploited in medicine, including veterinary medicine.

PONTYPOOL WARE

Torfaen County Borough Council is conserving some ancient Chestnut pollards at Pontypool. They are known to have been planted before 1700 which puts them into the period when Pontypool Park was owned by Major John Hanbury (1664-1734) who, pioneered a secret process for japanning iron. The Council believes these Chestnuts were cropped for making charcoal for use in the processing but nothing is known for sure, since the technique was a secret that "the family took with them to the grave." The present Sir Richard Hanbury Tenison confirmed that there was no mention of these trees in the Estate records,

reporting, "We have a pretty good idea of what was in our woods from around 1770 - in some cases earlier - and there is never any mention of chestnuts....Of course I plant a lot of chestnut now as the tree does well on our ground and doesn't shake." They sell it to timber mills and use it on the estate.

It was the English East India Company who first brought costly oriental lacquered goods into the country. This was especially so after the Restoration, when they became highly fashionable. Western, cheaper, imitations were soon being made, applied to paper, wood, leather and even slate. Applying it to metal was not possible - until the advent of Pontypool Ware. Major Hanbury employed a Northamptonshire manager, Thomas Allgood, who advanced metal working by developing a machine capable of rolling out thin iron sheets of even thickness. These were then coated with tin to prevent rusting, and lacquered with a new varnish based upon the by-products of the local coal industry. For three generations, up to 1790, his work made Pontypool famous and prosperous (and the work continued at Usk till 1820 - *Usk castle illus.*).

BIBLE

The spiritual values of trees in British ethnobotany are specific to those species familiar to the people of North West Europe who settled here. There were no vacancies in their view of things and so the Chestnut has never been given a role. The coming of Christianity did not change that, since the Chestnut is mentioned only twice in the Bible. The reference in Genesis 31: 37 in the Authorised Version read:- "And Jacob took him rods of green poplar, and of the hazel and chestnut tree....." (in a passage that is more important for being such an early description of the selective breeding of livestock). However, that reference has been amended in recent translations, such as the Good News Bible, to become Poplar. Almond and Plane. Similarly, the reference in Ezekiel 31:8 is now translated as Plane.

IN CONCLUSION

Sitting in the ruins of Bayham Abbey, on one of the first field trips for this study, there was no hint of the range of places that would soon need visiting; certainly not coal mines. The Chestnut tree has been full of surprises, not least for the wide range of topics associated with it and for the contribution it has made to both the visual and working landscape. Out of sight, there is an equally diverse set of scientists working to ensure a future for the tree and for ourselves. We typed four topics into the database of scientific papers published in English the previous year and the list printed out to forty-six A4 sheets! The vast majority of entries related to those remarkable little compounds called tannins. For well over a hundred years we have been exploiting their action in water, and that continues, but now science wants to know what they do in our bodies - have they got potential to heal health problems or to ward them off in the first place? Would it be advantageous to add them to food? We know already that the balance of amino acids in chestnuts is close to the presumed ideal for warding off heart problems but the potential is far wider than that. Alongside these enquiries are investigations into food allergies and nut allergies in particular. A parallel interest is being taken by veterinary sciences too. So the world of the Chestnut is not in such decline as the neglected coppices in the countryside would have us believe. These too are being given fresh consideration, for furniture, fuel, composite building materials, and so forth.

If we pause to look out on a wider world we notice that Britain is about the only country where the tree can be grown well that does not have nut orchards. In some countries the nut harvest makes a major contribution to the economy. This is all the more remiss when it is remembered that in Britain the tree has not had to battle against such major diseases as Chestnut Blight. With global warming it is presumed that this will not be the case for long but there is a research programme in place to combat this - except that we heard that it is on 'hold' awaiting funding. Other countries are well advanced in their efforts to combat these diseases. In America they have been working at it for decades but there has never been the incentive in Britain, since we have no history of nut orchards. That could change. There is now a whole new range of disease-resistant cultivars and hybrids on the market and many of these remain *small* trees or large shrubs. Some are available already in Britain. They would suit certain grant-aided schemes for planting more trees and keeping the countryside looking like countryside. They would make an interesting addition to the scene, as are the neglected coppices already. They are growing up fast to create new high-canopy woods that we have not had before. It will be interesting to see which species of wildlife adapt to this new habitat. The whole history of the British landscape, for thousands of years, has been one of continual change to suit our ever-changing needs and this will continue.

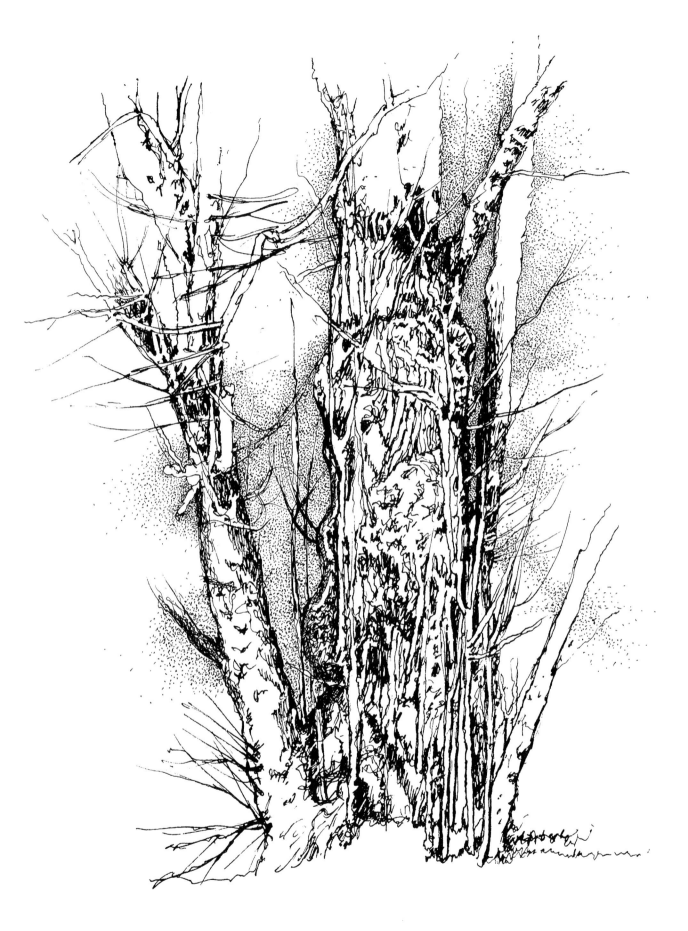

This specimen, about 120 years old, lost its top to storm damage and that has promoted a mass off side growths (epicormic growth) and basal suckers (from the root collar), some of which are growing up to become new trunks. It demonstrates how the multi-trunked veterans were created. This tree has produced a nightmare of twigs, which were reduced severely for the sketch.

Otttershaw Chase, Surrey

ACKNOWLEDGEMENTS

We haven't been able to list every single person who helped but the following people gave us information or guidance that was significant in the writing of the final text. Omitted from the list, at their own request, are those who trusted us to treat their information as 'non attributable' when their terms of employment included not giving information to outsiders. Some sources made valuable contributions in more than one category but are listed here under the heading to which they contributed the most. Apologies to anybody who does not have the correct title; we tried to remember to ask everybody how they would like to be styled.

ARCHAEOLOGY and METALLURGY
Alex Andews, Torfaen County Borough Council.
Valerie Fryer
Sir Richard Hanbury Tenison; Potypool Park Estates.
Jeremy Hodgkinson, Wealden Iron Research Group
A. Moffat, Gen. Sec., Kent Archaeological Society
Richard Osborn
Dr Gerry McDonnell, Senior Lecturer in Archaeological
  Sciences, Bradford University.
David Smith, Bristol and Gloucestershire Society

BOTANY
Dr Richard Bisgrove, Dept. of Horticulture; Reading
  University.
Dr Barbara Pickersgill, Dept. Agricultural Botany;
  Reading University.

COPPICING and COPPICE PRODUCTS
Ian Baldwin, Countryside Ranger, Waverley Borough
  Council.
Chestnut Fencing Manufacturers Society
John Faulker, Phoenix Walking Stick Co. Ltd
Stephen Homewood, J. E Homewood & Son

CULINARY and NUTRITION
Mrs B. Curtecka
Peter Cockerill
Nina Deal
Dr. Harry Nursten, School of Food Biosciences,
  University of Reading
Betty Tottenham
Dr Beverley Weston

DRILLING MUDS
Michael Hodder, UK Technical Services Manager, M-I
  Drilling Fluids
Andrew Kidd, Robin Westerman, and colleagues, Dept.
  of Petroleum Engineering, Heriot-Watt University,
  Edinburgh
Nabil Mazzawi
Kurt Nielsen
Sandie Maddux and colleagues at Halliburton.
Fred Paillet, Dept. of Geology, University of Maine
Bill Whitman

FLOORING
Global Reclamation Ltd
Clive Harrison, Frenchfloors, Harwich
Lee Mat Reclamation
David Scothern, Global Reclamation Ltd.
Parquet and General Flooring Co. Ltd
Redlam Timbers Ltd
Xylodom Wood Products

FORESTRY
Nigel Braden
Forest Enterprises
Forestry Commission, England/Scotland/Wales
Green Wood Trust
Donald Macdonald, Head Forester, Cowdray Estates
National Trust
Woodland Trust
Matthew Woodcock, Forestry Commission
  (S.E.England Conservancy)

FRUIT TREES
Clive Castell, BlueBell Nursery
Martin Crawford, Agroforestry Research Trust
Claire Higgins, Ken Muir Ltd.

FURNITURE
Eoin Cox MBE, Woodschool Ltd
David Gree; High Weald Furniture
J. Martin, Rustic Garden Furniture

HOPS
Alexa Barrow, Rural Life Centre, Tilford, Surrey
Samantha Cutter, Curator, Museum of Kent Life
Julia King, Puttenham and Wanborough Garden Club
Michael Leishman

LIBRARIES
Penny Hollow, Haslemere Educational Museum
Alice Holt Forest Research Station
Linda Ng, Library Ass., Halliburton & KBR
Laura Hastings, Dept. Economic Botany, Royal Botanic
  Gardens, Kew.
Tim Peacock, Derby Univ. library
Hazel Putland, Royal Horticultural Society, Wisley

MINING
Daz Beattie;
Peter Challis
Alan Dean, Cannock Chase Mining Historical Society
James Findlay
Mark Frost, Senior Assistant Curator, Dover Museum
Dr Jeremy Greenwood, University of Exeter
John Harvey, Deputy Gaveller, Forest of Dean
Alison Henesey, Librarian, National Coal Mining
  Museum for England
Barry Job
Kelvin Lake
D. Lloyd, Rhondda Heritage Park, Lewis Merthyr
Colliery
Peter Mason (ref. East Kent Coalfield)
Bernard Moore
Tony Oldham (ref. Forest of Dean)
D.R.Poyner
Chris Rees, Cefn Coed Colliery Museum
Martin Roe, Conservation Officer, National Association
  of Mining History Organisations
Rick Stewart;
Alan Vickers (ref. Durham mining)
Paul Wells, Kent Underground Research Group

NURSERIES
Martin Crawford, Agroforestry Research Trust
Clive Simms
Oakover, Ashford, Kent

PAPER
Michael Henderson, St Regis Paper Company Ltd.,
Sudbrook.

PARKS AND GARDENS
Nina Deal
Sarah Couch, Historic Landscape Consultant
Brenda Lewis;, Historic parks and gardens Officer, Surrey
  County Council.
National Trust
National Trust for Scotland
Surrey Gardens Trust

TANNINS/TANNING/LEATHERWORKING
Matthew Abbott, Joseph Clayton & Son (Chesterfield)
Ltd.
Roger Barlee, J. H. Hewit & Sons Ltd, Edinburgh
Brian Corderey, B.C.Leathers Ltd; Frinton; Essex
Dr Irene Mueller-Harvey, Dept. Agriculture, Reading
University
Steven Porter, Orthotist
John Williams, Secretariat, International Council of
Tanners.
J. J. Williamson & Sons (Canterbury) Ltd.
Roy Winnard, Metropolitan Leather Co. Ltd. Thrapston,
  Northants

TIMBER
Malcolm Adkins, Coventry Boatbuilders and Chandlery
Nigel Braden, Nigel Braden Timber
Duffield Timber, North Yorkshire
Clive Harrison (hardwood floors)
Philip Stevens (musical instruments)

VITICULTURE
Mark Ebdon, Estate Manager, Painshill Park
Lamberhurst Vineyard, Kent.

WATER TREATMENT/BOILER SYSTEMS
Clive Evans, Kew Bridge Steam Museum
Michael Heintzman
Martin Nicholas
Nigel Nicholson

Saxon church, Albury Park

BIBLIOGRAPHY

BAILEY, A. R.;*Textbook of Metallurgy*; Imperial College of Science and Technology; 2nd ed. 1960

BARRETT, Helena and John Phillips; *Suburban Style: The British Home 1840-1960;* (publisher and date not printed)

BLACK, R.; 'Chestnut Coppice with Particular Reference to Layering' in Quarterly Journal of Forestry; 57; 1963

BOURDU, Robert; *le châtaignier*; Actes Sud; 1996

BOURNE, George; *The Bettesworth Book*; Duckworth; 1911 ed.

BOWN, D.; *Encyclopaedia of Herbs and their Uses;* Dorling Kindersley; 1995

BRAID, J.; 'The Sweet Chestnut as a Timber Tree'; Journal of Ecology; V; 1911

BRAUN, Hugh; *Old English Houses*; Faber and Faber; 1962

BREWER E. C.; *A Dictionary of Phrase and Fable;* Galley Press ed.; 1988

BROWN, R. J.;*The English Country Cottage*; Hamlyn; 1979

CHANCELLOR, P. M.; *Handbook of the Bach Flower Remedies*; C. W. Daniel Co. Ltd.; 1985

CHEVALLIER, A.; *The Encyclopaedia of Medicinal Plants*; Dorling Kindersley; 1996

CHIEJ, R.; *Encyclopaedia of Medicinal Plants*; MacDonald; 1984

CLAPHAM, A. R. et al; *Flora of the British Isles*; CUP; 1962

COX, J. C.; *The Royal Forests of England*; 1905

CRAWFORD, Martin; *Chestnuts: Production and Culture*; Agroforestry Research Trust; 1995

DANNATT, N.; *Marketing Coppice and Other Small Roundwood in S. E. England*; Forestry Comm.; 1991

DEFOE, Daniel; *A Tour Through the Whole Island of Great Britain*; Penguin; 1971 ed.

DOWSETT, J Morewood ; *The Romance of England's Forests;* John Gifford Ltd; 1943

DUCAREL, A. C. and THORPE, J. (1772) 'A Letter Concerning Chestnut Trees' in Phil. Trans. Royal. Society. London; 61; 136-169

EDLIN, Herbert; *British Woodland Trees*; Batsford; 1944

EDLIN, Herbert; *Forestry and Woodland Life*; Batsford; 1948

EVELYN, John; *Silva: A Discourse of Forest Trees*; 1662

FACCIOLA; S.; *Cornucopia-A Source Book of Edible Plants*; Kampong Publications; 1990

FASTNEDGE, Ralph; *English Furniture Styles 1500-1830; Penguin; 1955*

FELBRIDGE and District History Group; *Felbridge, Parish and People Millenium Edition*; Felbridge Parish Council, 1999

FERN, Ken; *Plants for a Future*; Permanent Publications; 1997

FILMER, Richard; *Hops and Hop Picking*; Shire 1982

FLAVELL, Linda and Roger; *The Chronolgy of Words and Phrases: A Thousand Years in the History of English*; Silverdale Books; Leicester; 1999

FORD, E. and NEWBOULD, P.; 'The Biomass of Ground Vegetation and its Relation to Tree Cover Through a Deciduous Woodland Cycle' in Journal of Ecology, 65; 1977 pp.201-12

FORESTRY COMMISSION; *Census of Woodland and Trees 1979-82*; Forestry Commission, Edinburgh; 1984

FORESTRY COMMISSION; *National Inventory of Woodland and Trees 1995-99*; Forestry Commission; Edinburgh; 2001

FRANK, Robert Worth, 'The "Hungry Gap," Crop Failure, and Famine....' in SWEENEY, Del. ed., *Agriculture in the Middle Ages*, Univ. of Pennsylvania Press; 1995

FURNELL, Denis; *Health from the Hedgerow: A Naturalist's Encyclopaedia of Medicinal Plants*; Batsford; 1985

GLOAG, John; *A Short Dictionary of Furniture*; Allen and Unwin; 1952

GODWIN, Sir Harry, *History of the British Flora*; CUP; 2nd ed. 1975

GRAY, George R.and DARLEY, H. C. H.; *Composition and Properties of Oil Well Drilling Fluids*; 4th ed. Gulf Pub. Co. 1980

GRIGSON, Geoffrey; *A Dictionary of English Plant Names*; Allen Lane; 1974

GRIFFIN, Nicola; *The Survival of the Sweet Chestnut Coppice Industry in England*; Report for Coventry Polytechnic; 1985

GROVES, Arthur H.; 'The Brooklyn Botanic Gardens Chestnut Breeding Project'; in *35th Annual Report of Northern Nut Growers Association*; 1944; pp.22-31

HADFIELD, Miles; *A History of British Gardening*; Hutchinson & Co., 1960

HART, G. E.; *Royal Forest: A History of Dean's Woods as Producers of Timber*; Clarendon Press, Oxford; 1966

HARVEY, John; *Medieval Gardens;* Batsford; 1981

HOPMAN, E.E.; *Tree Medicine Tree Magic*; Phoenix (Washington USA); 1991

HOUSE, Frank H.; *Timber at War*; Ernest Benn Ltd; 1965

HOWARD, A.; *Trees in Britain and their Timbers*; Country Life; 1947

HOWES; F. N.; *Vegtable Tanning Materials*; Butterworth's Scientific Publications; 1953

HOWES, F.N.; *A Dictionary of Useful and Everyday Plants and their Common Names*; CUP; 1974

HOWKINS, Chris; *Trees, Herbs and Charcoal Burners*; Chris Howkins; 1994

HUGHES, Herbert W.; *A Text Book of Coal Mining*; Charles Griffin; 1901

HULME, F. Edward; *Wild Fruits of the Country-side*; Hutchinson; 1902

JEKYLL, Gertrude, *Old West Surrey*; Longmans, Green and Co; 1904

KITZ, Norman and Beryl; *Pains Hill Park: Hamilton and his picturesqe landscape*; Norman Kitz; 1984

LEVY, Juliette de Bairacli; *The Illustrated Herbal Handbook;* Faber; 1974

LEWINGTON, Anna, *Plants For People*; Natural History Museum Publications; 1990

LINDSAY MARKETING SERVICES (UK) Ltd; Report for the Forestry Commission, *The Marketing of Chestnut Coppice Products in S. E. England*; 1993

LOUDON, J.; *Observations of the Formation and Management of Useful and Ornamental Plantations...*; Longman, Hurst, Rees and Orme; 1804
An Encyclopaedia of Trees and Shrubs; Longmans; 1842

LOVETT, Maurice; *Bewing and Breweries*; Shire; 1981

LOWENFELD, Claire; *Britain's Wild Larder – Nuts*; Faber and Faber; 1957

MACLEAN, M.; *Hedges*;

McLEAN, Teresa; *Medieval English Gardens*; Barrie and Jenkins; 1989

MARSHALL, W.;*The Rural Economy of the Southern Counties;* Vols I & II; 1798

MEE, Arthur ed.; *The King's England: Surrey*; Hodder and Stoughton; 1938

MEIGGS Russell, *Trees and Timber in the Ancient Mediterranean World*, OUP. 1982

MELLING, John; *London's Guilds and Liveries*; Shire; 1973

MOERMAN, Daniel; *Native American Ethnobotany*; Timber Press; 1998

MORRIS, J.;*Domesday Book*; Vol 15: Gloucestershire; Phillimore; 1982

MORRIS, Marc; *Castle - A history of the Buildings that shaped Medieval Britain*; Cannel Four Books; 2003

MOTTRAM and RADLOFF, *Food Tables*; Arnold; 1937

MUIR, W. A.; *1945, Forestry*; Forestry Commission; Vol 19; 1945; pp. 74-85

PACKHAM, John and HARDING, D.; *Ecology of Woodland Processes*; Arnold; 1982

PARKER, H. H.; *The Hop Industry*; King & Son, 1934

PEATY, Ian; *You Brew Good Ale: A History of Small-scale Brewing*; Sutton Publisjing; 1997

PEVSNER, Nikolaus and NAIRN, Ian; *The Buildings of England: Sussex*; Penguin, 1965

RACKHAM, Oliver; *Trees and Woodland in the British Landscape*; Dent; 1976
Ancient Woodlands; Arnold; 1980
History of the Countryside; Dent; 1986

RICHARDS, E. G.; *The Growing of Hardwoods for Pulpwood*; Quarterly Journal of Forestry. Vol 55; 1961, pp.206-222

ROACH, F. A.; *Cultivated Fruits of Britain*; Blackwell; 1986

(Illus: hedgehog above and five silhouettes from the mines visits)

ROLLINSON, T.J.D. and J. EVANS; *The Yield of Sweet Chestnut Coppice*; Forestry Commission Bulletin 64; 1987

RHS; *The New Royal Horticultural Society Dictionary of Gardening*; Macmillan; 1992

ROOM, Adrian; *Dictionary of Proper Names*; Cassell; 1992

SALZMAN, L. F.; *Building in England down to 1540*; 1952 (enlarged ed. 1967)

SCOT, Reynolde; *A Perfite Platform of a Hoppe Garden*; 1574, 1576, 1578

SEFRIOUI, Anne, *Vaux le Vicompte*; Editions Scala; Paris. n.d.

SEYMOUR, John; *The Forgotten Arts*; Dorling Kindersley edition; 1984

STACE, Clive; *New Flora of the British Isles*; CUP; 1991

STOKES, Jon; *Great British Trees*; the Tree Council; 2002

STUART, Malcolm ed.; *The Encyclopaedia of Herbs and Herbalism*; MacDonald; 1987

STURT, George; *Small Boy in the Sixties*; CUP; 1932 ed.

VICTORIA COUNTY HISTORY - vols for Gloucestershire, Surrey and Sussex

WALLIS; T. E.; *A Textbook of Pharmacognosy*; J.& A Churchill Ltd.; 1951

WILKS, J. H.; *Trees of the British Isles in History and Legend*; Muller; 1972

YOUNG, Geoffrey; *Traditional British Crafts*; Marshall Cavendish; 1989

INDEX

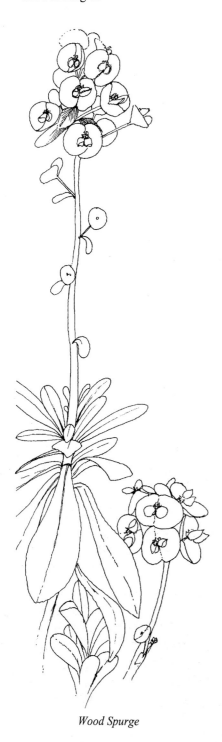

Wood Spurge